My Kid Eats Everything!

The Journey from Picky to Adventurous Eating

SUSAN L. ROBERTS, M.DIV., O.T.R./L.

My Kid Eats Everything: The Journey from Picky to Adventurous Eating
Copyright © 2011 by Susan L. Roberts, M.Div., O.T.R./L.

ISBN 978-0-9846847-00
ISBN-13: 978-0984684700

DEDICATION

For all the families, children, therapists and other caregivers who have taught me as much as I have taught them.

Thank-you for joining me on this journey.

TABLE OF CONTENTS

A GRATITUDE LIST

Although writing takes place in solitude, no author writes alone. I owe a great deal of thanks to all of the people who helped me with this book.

Cross Country Education has supported me in the presentation of my seminar "Mealtime Success for Kids on the Spectrum: Holistic Nutrition for Picky Eaters" for the past several years. That course led to a six-month long teleseminar called, "My Kid Eats Everything." This book comes directly out of those experiences. Thanks goes to all those who attended my courses and shared their experiences and questions.

Many professional caregivers have written and lectured about the various topics that I include in this book. I stand on the shoulders of Ellyn Satter, Kay Toomey and Marsha Dunn Klein – true experts in the field of children's nutrition and creative mealtime solutions. Any discrepancies or errors in this book rest solely with my interpretation of their work.

I embarked on my own professional journey to nutrition by enrolling at the Institute for Integrative Nutrition in 2009. Thanks go to the Institute's founder, Joshua Rosenthal, for living out his vision of nutrition that encompasses not just the mind and body, but the spirit and soul as well. That vision and the amazing lecturers who spoke to us during my year of study provided a firm foundation for creating a holistic model of mealtimes and nutrition.

Children with autism have taught me more about this mealtime journey than anyone else. Stanley Greenspan and Barry and Samharia Kaufmann's creative approaches to autism shine a bright light on the importance of paying attention to what children communicate. Their somewhat different but equally respectful attitudes inform all aspects of my work.

Thanks to Steve Cox for suggesting that I open the book with a story. I added one to each chapter and the book is better for it. Thanks to Bea Coryell, Kendra Moore, Jane Kingsley, Jean Weigle, and Leila Power for reading the first drafts of this book and sharing some of their own stories about "picky eating." Thanks to Ruth Storti for proofreading the final copies and getting it ready for print.

Most of all thanks to my business advisors Nancy Cooper and Marsha Stone for the encouragement and inspiration that fueled the project even when I got tired and had doubts. Even more thanks go to Marsha, my wife, who made the financial and temporal space that allowed me to complete this project. What a great sixtieth birthday present!

INTRODUCTION

Zoey refused to eat anything but cheese flavored puffs and a dietary supplement she drank from her favorite sipping cup until just before her third birthday when the family gathered to celebrate Passover. Zoey sat on her beloved grandfather's lap as everyone read the Haggadah (Passover story). When her grandpa put some horseradish on a matzo and passed it around the table Zoey grabbed a piece for herself. Before anyone could react Zoey had popped the spicy cracker into her mouth, chewed and swallowed it. Zoey loved horseradish! For months she would eat anything that had horseradish on it.

Mystified by Zoey's new food choice, Zoey's father asked her occupational therapist and registered dietician if they could figure it out. The occupational therapist pointed out that Zoey liked lots of intense sensory experiences like spinning on the swing and crashing on the tumbling mats. Her registered dietician noted that Zoey might have a zinc deficiency so she could only taste strong flavors. Zoey's therapist included more spinning, tumbling and jumping into Zoey's therapy sessions. The registered dietician recommended a zinc supplement in addition to Zoey's regular multi-vitamin. Together the three adults planned ways to introduce new flavorful foods to Zoey's diet and within a year Zoey ate like all the other members of her family.

If you are picking up this book, chances are you worry about the selective way your child eats. Probably she does not "eat everything" you serve her[1]. In fact she may only eat a handful of "favorite" foods;

---

1   A note on gender identified pronouns: I want to keep the language in this guidebook simple and clear. Gender identified pronouns help me to do this.

1

mostly the kinds of processed foods and sweets most parents identify as "bad" for kids.

Your child may be overweight or underweight, getting frequent colds, cranky, tired and not interested in playing outside.

Your child may be hyperactive, may have trouble getting along with other children, or may be unable to attend to any activity other than video games for more than a few minutes.

Your child may even have drifted into a world you cannot understand, a place where you cannot seem to reach her with hugs, play or words of love.

You may have asked your pediatrician about your child's eating habits and been told not to worry, "she'll grow out of it."

Or you might have been told to let your child get hungry – "and then she'll eat."

Some of you may even have been advised to use liquid dietary supplements.

A few of you have been threatened with the idea of putting in a "feeding tube" and some of your children already have one.

Whoever you are, you worry about what your child eats. You want her to eat more variety and make healthier choices and so far nothing seems to be working.

This book is for you.

Welcome to a great adventure. I'm excited to be joining you by providing this guide book. At the end of our journey you, your special child, and the rest of your family will have a whole new appreciation of food – and of the joys of eating. Together we will discover:

1. Why your child chooses the foods she chooses;
2. Which foods make her feel best;
3. How to choose healthier foods for her body;
4. Ways to ENJOY trying new foods; and
5. The pleasures of sharing a meal with family and friends.

Once we accomplish these goals your child will eat a wider variety of foods and naturally make healthier choices.

I promise you lots of fun along the way.

I want you to know something about me – your guide on this adventure.

Even numbered chapters will use female identified gender pronouns for children and male identified pronouns for adults. Odd numbered chapters will reverse this by using male identified pronouns for children and female identified pronouns for adults.

I come from a family of "adventurous eaters" – so I know how to approach unfamiliar foods safely and with a sense of exploration.

I married into a family of "picky eaters" so I know the frustration of preparing "good" food and having to eat alone or even throw it away.

I have worked my entire adult life helping children with mealtime challenges at home and in schools. Most of these children carried labels that strike fear into the hearts of parents. Labels like: autism, cerebral palsy, muscular dystrophy, *spina bifida*, ADHD, and mental retardation.

If your child carries such a label, relax, this book will address your children's issues. If your child is a picky eater "for no good reason," we'll find ways to turn her into a healthy eater by learning to enjoy trying new foods and sharing meals with friends and family.

I am probably old enough to be your child's grandmother – and as an occupational therapist I have seen a lot of behaviors and spent plenty of time working with parents, teachers, caregivers and other therapists figuring out how to address the ways kids approach food. The stories I tell at the beginning of each chapter use details from these experiences. I have rearranged details and names to protect the anonymity of individuals. I hope you see your picky eater in some of these stories and that this guidebook helps solve your family's challenges.

I have had a lifelong interest in healing rituals[2] and how these work by activating our senses to change the way we think and feel. All cultures have special foods, rituals and remedies that involve eating. In the past we may have discounted some of the "old" ways, but contemporary research confirms and explains why these traditional foods, rituals and remedies cause positive changes in overall health. We will use both traditional approaches and modern science to unravel your child's "picky eating" and start her on a path to "adventurous eating."

I owe a great debt to many people who have been my guides on this journey. Although I will not footnote every reference to specific books or research papers, I have included a few resources at the end of each chapter and the entire list at the end of the book. I recommend every one and I hope you take the time to explore some of these resources as well.

PREDICTABLE STAGES ON THE JOURNEY

Children often act in novel, unique, creative, interesting, charming and unpredictable ways. Your child will certainly behave this way. I

---

2   My definition of "healing rituals": Any repetitive set of activities or behaviors (in Western medical practice or "traditional" non-Western, non-medical practices) applied to the client (sufferer, victim or patient) in the event of trauma, illness, disease or discomfort.

believe that all children grow in patterns that tend to repeat themselves and I will show you these patterns as we go on this journey together. I hope these patterns will help you make sense of your child's novel, unique, creative, interesting and charming behaviors so that you can see progress even on those days when it seems that nothing has changed.

Brand Name "Grazers" – Your child eats sporadic mini-meals and snacks throughout the day ("grazing" in nutrition speak) and probably eats only a few very specific brand name foods. You may have tried putting a similar food into the same packaging, but your picky eater could tell the difference right away.

Similar Food "Grazers" – Your child eats a variety of brand name foods and with some foods will eat any brand and maybe even a version of this food prepared at home. Your child may reluctantly sit at the table, but prefers to eat in front of TV whenever she is hungry (in other words, "grazing").

Eats with Family – Your child will sit at the table during regular mealtimes and snack at regular times, but you prepare her special foods and snacks in-between times because she still refuses to eat like the rest of the family.

Eats Most Foods with Family – Your child eats meals and snacks at regular times at home and in school. Your child eats many of the same foods that the rest of the family eats, but still has some fears or cautious behavior about trying new foods.

Tries New Foods – Your child eats meals and snacks at regular times at home and in school. She may not eat a new food, but she will "try" a new food without prompting.

Joyfully Anticipates Trying New Foods – Your child looks forward to holiday meals and the special foods your family only eats during these times. If an unfamiliar dish finds its way onto the holiday table your child either politely declines or eagerly tries the unfamiliar food.

My Kid Eats Anything! – Your child leads the way and encourages other children to try new foods at neighborhood barbecues, birthday parties and ethnic restaurants.

This guidebook aims to start wherever you find yourself in one of the first four stages and get your child to the fifth stage, *Tries New Foods*. This will take some effort on your part, but once your family has gotten into a habit of family meals and trying new foods you will find you can choose to take your family even further on the journey to "adventurous eating." Most families want to go at least as far as *Joyfully Anticipates Trying New Foods,* but fun-loving adventurers may continue until you can joyfully declare *"My Kid Eats Anything!"*

4

If your family eats in your picky eater's favorite fast food restaurant, where she only orders chicken nuggets with ketchup, probably a family outing to your neighborhood's new Ethiopian restaurant seems as reasonable as a trip to the moon. I wish for your family that you take this journey as far as you can. Sharing food together with friends and family nourishes our bodies and our souls. You will find family meals one of the great pleasures of living.

PLAYING BY THE RULES

This guidebook will ask you to abide by my "four VERY STRICT rules." I will summarize each chapter's information around these rules. As far as I am concerned these are the ONLY rules. Let's keep it simple.

1. *HAVE FUN.* We want our mealtimes to be joyous affairs that nourish our souls as well as our bodies. The guidebook will show you a fun-filled route to healthy eating. You will need to figure out how to bring this sense of fun to your child and your family. Each chapter will provide some entertaining approaches to mealtime issues that you can adapt to fit your family's sense of fun.

In general the best way to have fun with your child is to give up ALL of your expectations. Hold onto hope (see Rule #4) but stay in the moment and bring your *energy, excitement,* and *enthusiasm*[3] to every mealtime experience. Remember to approach this journey as an adventure and come to the experience wearing "party clothes."

2. *PLAY SAFELY.* If your child is a "picky eater" eating has probably become stressful or even scary for her. This guidebook will help you figure out what foods feel "comfortable" to your child and why. It will help you increase the number of "new" foods your child eats and make sure those new food choices

---

3   The Son-Rise Program® uses the words *energy, enthusiasm* and *excitement* to describe an "attitude" they have found essential for helping families with severely disabled children make amazing changes in their lives. I have adopted the admonition to "hold onto hope," "leave behind expectations," and "bring the three E's (*energy, excitement* and *enthusiasm*) from the Son-Rise Program®. They don't yet have many published papers in scientific journals, but they do have a 40 year track record that started with their own son, and current CEO of the Option Institute/Autism Treatment Center of America. Please visit their website: www.autismtreatmentcenter.com where you will find a wealth of inspiring stories and helpful advice, as well as many books about their experiences.

contribute to her overall health and vitality, based on sound nutritional advice and research. To do this you need some structure – so print out worksheets from the accompanying CD to organize these important concepts in a way that allows you to apply them and build on them throughout the journey.

3. ***MAKE FRIENDS.*** If you have an antagonistic relationship with your child at mealtimes this guidebook will help you change that. Humans have thrived on enjoying mealtimes together for roughly three million years. Our health depends on our positive relationships with others. How will you do that? Refer to rule #1. Each chapter will have activities and ideas for improving relationships among family members.\

4. ***USE IMAGINATION.*** Creativity gets us in touch with our soul. In every chapter you will find creative ideas for enjoying mealtimes. Lots of children and their caregivers have shared fresh ideas with me over the years, and now I get to share them with you. All our food needs to be "soul food" prepared with love and shared with a spirit of generosity. Keep hope alive by imagining your child enjoying family meals and eagerly trying new foods, but do your imagining AWAY from the table. At meals you must stay in the moment, without expectations. Believe in miracles. They happen every day.

USING THE FORMS

I have included forms in the book so that you see them as you go along. Many are printed across two pages and some are printed filled in as samples. I recommend that you download a copy of all the blank forms from my website. You can print the forms out and use multiple forms as you go along. Get the forms from: www.susanlroberts.com/mkee forms/html.

Are you ready for your BIG FOOD ADVENTURE?

I hope so.

LET'S GET STARTED!

CHAPTER ONE

Preparing for the Journey

Third-grader William refused to eat anything other than pureed or mashed foods. Any crunchy or textured foods made him gag. Sometimes he gagged if other people ate crunchy foods while sitting next to him. He did well in his academic work and got good report cards. William never ate lunch at school because children made fun of his "baby" food. He complained that he did not have any friends. At home he played computer games and watched his favorite movies and shows on TV. Whenever his parents turned off the TV, he would simply roll his toy cars back and forth or figure out how to spin them like tops.

Concerned that he might be bullied, Williams's mother contacted a special clinic that treated children with mealtime issues. The dietician worked with the family and also recommended that William see the clinic's occupational therapist. It seemed that William's play behaviors and food choices resembled those of a much younger child. William's mother learned how to teach William games they could play together away from the computer and TV screens. She began getting William to help prepare his own meals, and also dishes to share with the whole family. Within a year William would eat a school lunch or one from home along with his class. He also began making friends and inviting classmates over to his house for play dates.

Food changes everything.

Before we embark on this journey, let us set an intention for healing. Healing begins with intention. Alternative medicine has relied on this understanding for millennium, and now modern science confirms it. Positive psychology abounds with studies on the beneficial effects of simple practices such as "affirmations" and "gratitude lists." Meditation and prayer provide powerful stress relief when used in the treatment of cancer and other chronic health challenges. I chose the title of this book as an affirmation. I want you to hear yourself when you read the title, "My Kid Eats Everything." I want you to feel this intention every time you say it.

From the middle ages and well into the modern era, travelers did not undertake arduous journeys for recreation, or even to check off items from a "bucket list". These hardy adventurers called themselves pilgrims and they left familiar surroundings and set off to foreign lands knowing that the journey would test their faith in their abilities as well as their beliefs. Many pilgrims took journeys to holy places for healing from illness and disease. Our modern hospital and hospitality industries both grew out of these pilgrimages.

I invite you to think of this journey as a pilgrimage. You will leave behind familiar habits and patterns on a quest for better health. You may try techniques that your child rejects – loudly and strenuously. Expect those moments and think of them as a bit of bad weather. Sunny days of happier, healthier children will follow. I promise you that.

I ask you to spend a few moments reflecting on this journey. You, your child and your family will embark on a pilgrimage and you want clarity about your starting point before taking the first step.

Start by spending several half hours playing with your child and really watching what he likes to do best. Is he exploring the world through his senses, banging, poking, bouncing, and putting everything he can find in his mouth? Is he exploring the world through movement, running, climbing, pushing, pulling, tumbling, and crashing into things? Does he like to see how things work, build towers, knock them down, and listen to the same story over and over again? Does he make up and follow games with rules? Does he prefer spending time with his friends more than with you? Join him in his play world and pay close attention.

Print out the "Mealtime and Play Behaviors" form or use the form at the end of this chapter. Go through the three columns of play behaviors first. First, highlight the toys, games, and movements your child chooses without any prompting from you. These are the things he likes to do. Now circle the things you can encourage him to do and the ones you would like him to do.

Then take a look at the column of mealtime behaviors. Highlight the behaviors your child seems to do most often. Circle the ones you wish he did more often.

Look at the highlights and circles as a whole. Are there more highlighted behaviors in one row than in other rows or do they skip around all over the place? Does one row across have more circles than the other rows?

Play behaviors give us an accurate reading of a child's emotional maturity. Emotions, food, and mealtime intertwine together in an inseparable way. Understanding and accepting your child's emotional maturity will help you figure out reasonable expectations for mealtimes.

Highlighted areas represent what your child chooses. He chooses what his mind, body and spirit need in order to grow. The circles represent your expectations. How many circles do you find in the same rows as the highlighted areas? How many circles do you see in the rows above or below the highlighted areas? Do your expectations match your child's interests or do you tend to expect more or less emotional maturity than he has available?

I ask you to step outside of your role as a caretaker for the moment. You need to become a healer in order to be the guide your child and your family need for this journey. A healer holds on to *hope* and *intention*, and leaves *expectations* behind so she can stay in the moment. You need to bring healing energy into this endeavor. You need to put on your "party clothes" by bringing *energy, enthusiasm,* and *excitement* to every step of this journey. Some days you can do this easily, other days might prove more challenging and you may even need to take a day "off" now and then. Feel good about giving yourself a "break." Your *energy, enthusiasm,* and *excitement* will bring your child and your family through to the next step. Do these exercises only when you feel ready to put on your "party clothes!"

Most importantly, and EVERY day, let your *expectations* go. Ellyn Satter, a registered dietician, family therapist and guru of healthy eating for families, breaks down the responsibility of mealtimes into what works best. As a parent you get to be "the boss" of *what* foods to give to your child, *when* to give him food, and *where* he will eat. Your child gets to be "the boss" of *whether* he will eat, and *how much* he will eat. As long as you are choosing *what, when* and *where* to eat, you fulfill your job as a parent. As soon as you push your agenda of *whether* and *how much* your child should eat, you have moved into the realm of expectations. You have overstepped your child's boundaries and he will undoubtedly push back. Hold on to hope until it becomes faith. Do your job and trust your child to do his job.

I can't know your role in the family of the picky eater who stimulated you to buy this book so I will refer to you as "chief cook and bottle washer." You are someone who has some responsibility for buying groceries, preparing meals, and cleaning up after them. You have signed on to do some extra work. I bless you for that, and one day your picky eater will bless you as well.

Now it is time to step outside that role and take on the mantle of the healer.

Find a quiet moment in your day to physically set your intention for this journey. Wait until your child falls asleep, or get up early enough in the morning to have fifteen minutes of uninterrupted time. Stay late at the office or lock yourself in the bathroom. Do whatever you need to do to get a moment of peace.

Engage your sense of joy by treating yourself to a bubble bath, a favorite beverage or a lovely piece of chocolate; light a candle, put some flowers in a vase. Make yourself present for this special moment when you step through a doorway into the shoes of a holy person, healer, shaman, or medicine person.

Breathe deeply and make yourself ready. You will not do this alone. Ask for grace from the source of life, however you call it. Remember all of your ancestors and helpful friends and know that those memories will give you strength to succeed in this pilgrimage.

Get a pen and a piece of paper. Keep a journal of this pilgrimage if you like. It will be more exciting than any vacation you ever take. Whether you keep a journal or not, write the following.

Dearest child of mine,
After careful thought and consideration, I hereby promise to:
Honor your body as the temple of your soul
Offer you healthy foods and drinks
Realize that you deserve good health
Help you overcome habits that hurt you as much as they do me
Love and appreciate you for what you do
Accept that I have the power to help you heal yourself
Realize that laughter, play and rest help you feel good
And that sharing these moments with you will heal me as well.
Accept you and be grateful for you just the way you are
Listen to messages you send me when you are hurt or sick
Understand that my unexpressed emotions and thoughts affect you

List any additional promises:

_____ , I love you so much.
    Child's Name

Congratulations! You look FABULOUS in your "party clothes".

FREQUENTLY ASKED QUESTIONS:
Q: I don't get the connection between play, emotional maturity, and eating behaviors.

In the 1970s and 1980s we did not have any federally mandated early intervention or preschool programs for children with disabilities. Many five, six and seven year old children came to school unable to talk or walk. These children received speech, occupational, and physical therapy services. The physical therapists would come in and get children up in walkers and time after time these children started talking. Eventually we realized that something about walking (changing our perspective on the world) also stimulated and encouraged speech. We realized that it was more than just coincidence that caused children to walk and talk around the first year of life.

We also know that food and mealtimes have strong emotional associations for everyone. Play behaviors reflect emotional maturity quite accurately, and as the primary **occupation** of childhood serve to help children progress in their emotional, physical, social, and mental development. Occupational therapists use play to treat children (and often adults) recover from a whole host of disabling conditions. You will be using play as a vehicle to get your picky eater to enjoy trying new foods and you will probably find that doing so will improve other behaviors as well.

> ***Have Fun*** – Celebrate your child's unique strengths and your choice to act as your child's primary "healer."
>
> ***Play Safely*** – Take time to set a clear intention for healing.
>
> ***Make Friends*** – spend time playing with your child every day.
>
> ***Use Imagination*** – Believe in miracles. They happen every day whether we notice them or not.

Q: Do I really have to do all this ritual *mumbo jumbo*?

Of course you can do as many or as few of the exercises in this guidebook as you like. Getting in touch with what really works for you, your picky eater, and your family, forms the most essential lesson of this journey. Most healing rituals involve taking an inventory and leaving behind one way of life to begin a new one. In hospitals you do this filling out forms, taking off your clothes and putting on a special gown. Don't you think playing with your child and taking a bubble bath is a lot more fun? Try it and let me know what you think.

HEALING RESOURCES

Son-Rise: The Miracle Continues, by Barry Neil Kaufman. (1995). HJ Kramer Publishing. The story of how one family transformed their own lives and went on to help others through the Son-Rise Program®

Love, Medicine and Miracles: Lessons Learned About Self-Healing from a Surgeon's Experience with Exceptional Patients by Bernie Siegel. (1986) New York: HarperCollins Publishers Inc. A wonderful book about the healing power of love.

www.autismtreatmentcenter.org – the website for Son-Rise – chock full of wonderful information and tips that will help all parents, especially those whose children have special needs.

First, highlight the movement, games, and toys, your child chooses without any
your child to do. Highlight the mealtime behaviors your child seems to do most

"Vibration"	Mealtime Behaviors	Outdoor Play & Movement

Red
"Sensory"
	Frequent "on demand"
	    feedings,
	Liquids (milk or formula)
	Pureed foods (after 3-4
	    months)
	Messy-food falls out mouth
	Frequent choking
	Occasional spitting up
	Cries for food
		Limited outdoor time
		Learning to crawl, sit & stand
		Learning to push & pull
		Reaches for & grasps toys
		Explores with hands & mouth
		Enjoys rocking

Orange "Movement"	Eats small portions Eats on a schedule Sits in high chair Pureed to soft chopped food Drinks from a Sippy cup Messy-food falls out mouth Squeezes food with fingers Food falls off spoon Prefers single foods Avoids sticky foods Asks for foods by name	Walks, runs, climbs Throws & kicks balls Pushes wheeled toys Pulls wheeled toys Digs in dirt & sand Splashes in water Enjoys bouncing & swinging
Yellow "Construction"	Eats small portions Eats on a schedule Sits at a table Eats solid foods Drinks from a cup Uses a spoon Shows interest in a fork Wipes mouth Spills drinks Enjoys dipping foods Asks for food in sentences Says "please", "thank-you"	Jumps & hops Climbs up on slides Enjoys obstacle courses Throws balls at targets Catches balls sometimes Learns to ride a tricycle Makes messes in sand/mud Rough & tumble play Holds on to swing when swinging

Behaviors

prompting from you. Next circle the things you would like
often. Circle the ones you wish your child did more often.

Social Games with Others	Creative Play & Toys
Cuddling, bouncing & tickling Peek-a-boo Pat-a-cake Repeating sounds & words	Lullabies and soft voices Imitates facial expressions Enjoys lights on/off Attends to contrasts - black, white, bright colors Explores hands & feet Bangs to make noise Smells & tastes everything
Possessive of toys Demands adult attention Enjoys chase games Begins hide & seek games Asks for games & toys Puts toys away with help	Imitates adult actions Some "kitchen" play "Feeds" dolls/stuffed toys Makes toys "work" Pulls toys apart Scribbles on paper or wall Toys with lights & music
Wrestles with adults Plays next to children Sometimes shares toys Laughs at silly behavior Initiates chase games Enjoys hide & seek games Plays simple board games Asks why, what, when, who, where Puts toys away when asked	Elaborate kitchen games Elaborate car games Enjoys helping in kitchen Names toys Enjoys listening to stories Tells stories about toys/self Enjoys dress-up Builds with blocks Does 25 piece puzzles Learns to draw pictures Cuts paper & sister's hair Enjoys clay and dough

"Vibration"	Mealtime Behaviors	Outdoor Play & Movement
Green "Invention"	Small portions get larger Remembers meal schedule Sets table Occasional spills pouring or carrying liquids Learns to cut own meat Clears table Washes dishes Makes own sandwiches Converses at table Remembers "manners" Asks to leave table	Plays hopscotch & tag Jumps rope Skips & learns dance steps Skates & skis Hikes Climbs trees and structures Makes obstacle courses Hits targets often with ball Catches ball most of time Learns to ride a bike Builds forts & tree-houses Propels self on swings
Blue "Conformity"	Portions get larger May "skip" meals Makes own lunch Makes simple dinners Conversations need prompts Forgets "manners" Leaves table to join friends Brings friends home	Tests physical limits of endurance, strength Defies gravity Practices special skills May seem "clumsy" with growth spurts Enjoys watching others compete
Purple "Relationship"	Portions get much larger then stabilize May begin "dieting" Makes dinners for family Converses about interests "Manners" better away from home Eats out with friends Cooks meals for friends	Continues testing limits of endurance, strength, gravity, elements Develops special skills Clumsiness gradually disappears Learns to drive

Look at the highlights and circles as a whole. Are there more highlighted place? Does one color have more circles than the other colors? Highlighted areas his mind, body and spirit. The circles represent your expectations. How many How many circles went in the colors above or below the highlighted areas? Do tend to choose different colors?

Social Games with Others	Creative Play & Toys
Plays games with "rules"	Shares "pretend" with peers
Makes up "rules" for games	Writes name
Follows others "rules"	Illustrates stories
Shares & trades toys	Writes simple stories
Enjoys many board games	Makes up simple "plays"
Enjoys simple card games	Uses scissors, glue, paint &
Plays "team" sports	other media in art
	Plays an instrument
	Invents sandwiches
	Learns to use adult tools
Games with complex rules	Invents drama with others
Same-sex friendship	Detailed drawings
networks	Builds complex structures
Enjoys collections/trading	Sews, knits, other crafts
Board games with strategy	Writes songs
Card games with points	Experiments with recipes
Plays organized sports	Reads about sports, sci-fi,
Plays in orchestra or band	fantasy, famous people
Gaming networks	Drama becomes theater
Co-ed friendship networks	Drawings become artwork
Dating and gossiping	Structures become
Collections become lifelong	architecture &
"interests"	engineering
Plays organized sports	Crafters become artisans
Plays in orchestra or band	Songwriters become
	musicians
	Recipes lead to cooking

behaviors in one color or do they skip around all over the
represent the "vibration" your child needs right now to grow
circles do you find in the same colors as the highlighted areas?
your expectations match your child's "vibrations" or do you

SUSAN L. ROBERTS

CHAPTER TWO

Why Is My Child Such a Picky Eater & Where Can I Go for Help?

Darlene ate nothing but pizza, fish shaped crackers, fruit smoothies, and eggs cooked without any "flat" spots. Her parents worried about her health but learned how to cook eggs over gentle heat, stirring constantly to get just the texture she liked. Well-meaning grandparents told Darlene's father he should stop catering to his daughter and teach her to eat like regular people. They advocated letting her wait until she got hungry and offer her only foods the rest of the family ate. In fact they reminded him that they had forced him to finish his meals or else he would have to eat them the next meal. He tried that approach for a week until Darlene began refusing everything, except the fish-shaped crackers she got for snacks. Her health deteriorated and her doctor prescribed a liquid nutritional supplement and recommended that the family go to a special clinic that treated children with mealtime issues.

At the clinic the family learned that Darlene had several food sensitivities that made eating very uncomfortable. She also avoided touching any kind of gooey substances (like finger paint) and had difficulty chewing. Darlene saw the gastroenterologist, immunologist, speech therapist, occupational therapist, and behaviorist. Her parents also worked with the registered dietician to plan what foods would best get her back to health. The family learned how to prepare meals that avoided using ingredients that caused Darlene's indigestion and games that helped her develop better chewing skills and get over sensitivities to

19

textures. Within a year Darlene had progressed to eating twice as many foods as she had previously eaten and stopped needing the liquid dietary supplement.

Children become picky eaters for good reasons, not solely to create aggravation in the lives of their parents and caregivers. Children become picky eaters for biomedical and sociocultural issues that may have little or no relationship to parenting techniques. Before going any further on this journey, let's examine some of the reasons your child developed into a "picky eater."

We start with two definitions. When therapists and other health professionals talk about children with eating issues, they usually refer to "picky eaters" and "problem feeders."

"Picky eaters" eat forty or more different foods. Sometimes "picky eaters" go on a "food jag" where they only eat one food exclusively for a few days or weeks. Then they stop eating that food – for a while, sometimes as long as a week, a month or six months. Eventually "picky eaters" will start eating their formerly "favorite" food again.

"Problem feeders" eat less than forty different foods. "Problem feeders" also go on "eating jags," eating one food exclusively for days, weeks or months. Then they stop eating that food and they NEVER eat it again. Slowly they whittle away at the variety of foods they eat until they end up like Darlene, who started out eating a restricted, but more or less balanced diet and ended up on a "starvation" diet of crackers and water. Children who get to this point cannot take in enough nutrients to think and grow, even with vitamins. They need immediate attention.

Differentiating between "picky eaters" and "problem feeders" requires some professional assessment and diagnostic work so for most of this guidebook I will refer to both groups of children as "picky eaters." Whenever I use "problem feeder" it will denote those children at most serious nutritional risk, that is, children and parents who need professional help.

If your child eats fewer than forty different foods and that number gets smaller every week, tell your pediatrician your child has become a "problem feeder." Show the doctor your food journal. (I'll show you how to compile a food journal in Chapter 5.) Demand that your child get further evaluation from other health professionals – like a registered dietician, speech pathologist, occupational therapist or gastroenterologist. By the end of Chapter 5 you will have a pretty clear idea why your child is having so much difficulty at mealtimes and whether or not you can manage these problems yourself – and if you cannot, which professionals will best help you and your child.

All children have amazing bodies! They compensate for poor food choices in marvelous and ingenious ways. My cousin ate nothing but Captain Crunch cereal (with milk) and "egg foo young" (on Saturdays) until he was ten years old. He grew up just fine, finished college, got a good job and competes in half-marathons (13.5 miles of running!) at fifty. Not only that – he never even caught a cold until he was in fifth grade – even when his siblings got sick. As an adult he eats a wide variety of foods and enjoys gourmet cooking.

Print out the "Health Checklist" form or use the forms at the end of Chapter Three and Chapter Four. In these next two chapters you will look for signs that your child is thriving – in spite of what she currently eats. You can examine these signs of nutritional health yourself – without any assistance from a "professional." As a parent, you decide to get help for your child based on what you see and what you "feel." Trust your parental instincts and keep asking questions until you get answers that satisfy you. Ask other parents of picky eaters which professionals have helped them. "Picky eating" can negatively affect your child in many different ways. "Problem feeding" could signal a life threatening condition. Get help if you feel that you and your child need it.

The following professionals can help you in your search for answers.

Primary health care professionals include first and foremost your child's pediatrician or your family doctor. Other healthcare professionals may include nurses, naturopaths, homeopaths, acupuncturists, and chiropractors. Who do you go to for your day-to-day health concerns? Some healthcare professionals know more about nutrition than others. If your provider can't answer your questions, ask them to recommend another professional who can. These may include a gastroenterologist, neurologist, psychiatrist, nutritionist, or therapists of various kinds.

Nutritionists come in all shapes and sizes. A **Registered Dietician** has four to six years of university training in the properties and interaction of foods and their nutritional components. States usually require them to hold a license to practice which provides you with certain safeguards. They understand vitamins and other nutritional supplements and can recommend these. Some states require registered dieticians to work with a physician and others allow them to work independently.

"Nutritionists" do not have the same level of regulation as registered dieticians. Some nutritionists have studied the field in depth; others took "on-the-job training" from a vitamin manufacturer or food supplement retailer. Always ask for a nutritionist's background and training. You want a registered dietitian or a nutritionist who understands children and takes picky eating seriously. You want a professional who will work with your family, the way you cook and the way you eat, to help solve your child's picky eating problems.

Occupational Therapists help people do whatever they need to do to get through a day. Mealtimes and eating occupy a significant portion of everyone's day; so many occupational therapists specialize in these areas. For children, "play" occupies most of the day, and it serves to help them learn how to get along in the world. When an occupational therapist works with your child, it will look like "play." Occupational therapists take "play" very seriously. You want an occupational therapist who understands the "oral-motor" steps of breathing, sucking, swallowing and chewing as well as the "eye-hand" and "fine motor" skills of getting food into the mouth. Your occupational therapist needs to understand how your child "processes sensory information" and "integrates" it into mealtimes and eating. Look for "playful" therapy sessions that your child enjoys and ask to observe or participate so you can follow through with these therapy techniques at home.

Speech and Language Pathologists have in depth training on the structures and processes involved in developing language. All of these structures also play a part in eating. A speech therapist may specialize in swallowing and other aspects of eating as well as language development and articulation. You want a speech therapist who understands how to help a child with breathing, sucking, chewing and swallowing as well as how the sensory aspects of food (texture, flavor and smell) may affect this process. An effective speech therapist knows that "playful" therapy sessions help children learn these skills faster. Make sure your child has fun in therapy and ask to observe or participate so you can follow through with these therapy techniques at home.

Behaviorists come in more varieties than nutritionists. You may see a psychologist, social worker, counselor, teacher, ABA (Applied Behavioral Analysis) specialist, or a variety of these helping professionals. They will understand how social and emotional factors affect eating and have techniques for helping your child learn more effective mealtime behaviors. Find someone who understands your child and how you operate as a family during mealtimes. Children enjoy effective therapy sessions. Current research supports the idea that learning occurs in pleasurable environments. The learning that occurs under stressful conditions like fear or pain does not get processed into useful day-to-day behavioral strategies. If certain techniques make you or your child uncomfortable, look for another professional. Ask to observe or participate so you can follow through with behavioral techniques between sessions.

Physical Therapists can also play an important role in your child's journey to adventurous eating. Your child needs to sit up, breathe, chew and swallow – all of these activities involve coordination of many different muscles. Active play will also help your child develop an appetite. A physical therapist who understands children and the role of movement in developing mealtime skills can help children with weak muscles or poor coordination. Your physical therapist may not work directly on eating, but he will want to keep track of your child's progress in this area. Ask to observe or participate so you can help your child develop important movement skills between sessions.

FREQUENTLY ASKED QUESTIONS

Q: My child only eats chicken nuggets, bunny-shaped crackers and yogurt drinks but her doctor says this is O.K. What do you think?

We all need a combination of proteins, fats, and carbohydrates in our diets. Your doctor recognizes that the protein and fat in your child's chicken nuggets and yogurt drink provide these basic building blocks. Most of the carbohydrates in your child's diet come from sweets and white flour. Your doctor has probably recommended a multivitamin to make up for the lack of fruits and vegetables (more nutritious carbohydrates). Darlene's diet, though restricted to a few foods, did include fruit smoothies so she got some of the vitamins she needed that way. These restricted diets work in the short run, but losing a source of protein and fat (like the chicken nuggets, cheese, eggs, or yogurt could seriously affect a child's health as it did with

Have Fun – Forget about mealtimes, for now. Do something fun with your child. Something she enjoys.

Play Safely – Consider asking for advice from a professional or more experienced parent.

Make Friends – Talk to parents of picky eaters and those whose kids seem to eat everything.

Use Imagination – Think about what foods provide nourishment for your child. Of the ones she likes, which ones keep her healthy?

Darlene. This guidebook will help you expand your child's food choices and therefore protect her health over her lifetime.

Q: I take my child to therapy but she often cries and complains about having to go there. The therapist says that this is OK because he is asking her to do difficult tasks and most children struggle with learning these skills. Should we keep going to therapy?

Crying and complaining children do not learn new skills effectively and those skills they do learn to avoid discomfort do not enable them to use the skills they have learned in new situations. Challenges can frustrate us, but an effective therapy environment strives to achieve the "just right challenge," that is one that provides interest and novelty, as well as success. Stretching can pull muscles and long workouts might leave us tired. Discomfort that lasts more than a few hours or feeling exhausted usually causes more harm than good. Trust your child and your parental instincts. If your therapy sessions seem "painful" find another therapist. If you live somewhere with limited choices of therapists learn how to treat your child from books and videos; or work with a therapist over the phone or online.

HEALTH RESOURCES

The Portable Pediatrician's Guide to Kids: Your Child's Physical and Behavioral Development from Age 5 to Age 12 by Laura Nathanson. (1996). *New* York: Collins. You can find lots of books on young children, but this book provides a comprehensive common sense approach to school age children.

Quirky Kids: Understanding and Helping Your Child Who Doesn't Fit In – When to Worry and When Not to Worry by Perri Klass and Eileen Costello. (2004). New York: Ballantine. Two pediatricians with a common sense approach to childhood challenges.

www.eatright.org – The American Dietetic Association website has resources including how to locate a registered dietician in your area.

CHAPTER THREE

Trust the Body - Individual Biomedical Health Considerations

Two-year old Jason had trouble taking in nourishment from birth. He did not "latch on" to the nipple right away during his first few hours and hospital staff advised his mother to use a bottle and formula. Jason took in small amounts of formula and cried frequently through the night. He continued to have difficulty drinking from the bottle and eating pureed baby foods. When his mother started to give him more textured foods he began choking and refusing to eat. The day Jason's pediatrician pronounced him a case of "failure to thrive" Jason's mother described feeling those words like a "knife through her heart."

Jason's parents took him to a gastroenterologist who could not find any problems or food sensitivities. They took him to a neurologist who said everything seemed to be "working just fine." Eventually Jason went to the local hospital for a "swallow study" and his parents learned that he sucked so hard that liquids went into his trachea. He could not coordinate chewing so he sucked his solid foods as well, causing even more choking. Jason's parents took him several times a week to a speech pathologist at the hospital outpatient clinic. He learned how to chew and coordinate sucking, swallowing and breathing. By the time Jason reached his third birthday he could eat his cake and ice cream with no trouble at all.

Individually eating provides us with nutrients we need to support the growth and maintenance of our bodies. Our gastrointestinal system, the long tube that stretches from our mouth to our anus, takes in all kinds of foreign material. Most of this matter gets converted into nutrients that we use to produce energy for growing new cells, eliminating waste materials, powering our brains, and generally maintaining all of our bodily functions.

Things can go awry all along the gastrointestinal tract (GI tract), affecting the body's ability to process, move and utilize nutrients. Inflammation occurring anywhere along this tube can cause enough discomfort to make a child cautious and fearful about mealtimes. Picky eating behaviors often indicate this discomfort.

You might see sores or redness and swelling around your child's mouth or anus which could indicate inflammation of the gastrointestinal system. A gastroenterologist has tools that allow her to find inflammation elsewhere in the GI tract. You can help your doctors locate problem areas by giving them information about other symptoms you may see. We usually see the results of gastrointestinal and nutritional problems in the following ways. (Use the Health Checklist to help you keep track of how these may affect your child.)

ENERGY

What we eat provides our bodies with energy. Determine your child's energy levels with the following observations.

Movement – Children move around a lot. They stretch and build muscles, strengthen bones and exercise all of their senses by exploring the environment to learn how it works. If you and your child are not tired at the end of your child's day (especially toddlers) then probably your child isn't moving enough.

Sleep – Movement makes the body need rest. Your child may fight going to sleep, but once sleep overtakes them, you want to see them sleep through the night. Our bodies need eight to ten hours of rest every day in order to rebuild cells and stay healthy.

Mood – Children who have plenty of energy tend to act happier than those who don't have enough energy. Feeling tired and sick makes us all cranky and prone to "melt-downs."

Eyes – Some people say eyes are "windows to the soul." Certainly they give us an idea of energy levels. Look at your child's eyes. Look for bright, shiny, sparkling eyes that take in all of the environment – or at least those parts of the environment that interest your child the most.

Dull eyes, with dark circles and lids at "half-mast" indicate fatigue or illness.

GROWTH

Growing new cells takes more energy than any other process in the body. Keep track of how well your child grows with the forms from the national Center for Disease Control. You can download these from www.susanlroberts.com/mkee-forms.html.

Every summer my parents marked my height and my brothers' height on a door frame in the house my grandfather built up in Maine. Other door frames marked the growth of my mother and her older sister. All of our cousins had similarly marked doorways. Start this tradition with your own children using a strip of paper or cloth. Children need to grow every year until their growth levels off somewhere between the onset of puberty and their early to mid-twenties.

Your child's pediatrician has the Center for Disease Control form (or a similar one) in your child's medical chart. Each time your child goes to the doctor she will measure his height and weight and track it on this form. You can do the same thing at home two or three times a year. Look for a line of growth parallel to the lines on the chart; one that falls between the highest and lowest lines of the chart. A child's height (and weight) depends on the height (and healthy weight) of his parents. Short ancestors usually produce generations of short people – tall ancestors usually produce generations of tall people.

A child's height and weight needs to increase a couple of pounds every six months or so through childhood, every three months or so through puberty and level off towards the end of high school. When weight gain stops or decreases instead of steadily increasing, notify your pediatrician. If you complain to your pediatrician about your child's diet and hear "that's normal, don't worry about it" it means that your child falls in the right place for his age and he increases in height and weight along the line your doctor expects to see.

Proper growth indicates overall health better than many other indicators but nutritional deficiencies manifest elsewhere first because growth uses more energy than anything else the body does. Growth gets first "dibs" on the nutrients our body makes from the food we eat. The "Health Checklist" will help you spot potential problem areas so you can point these out to your doctor before your child's nutrition affects his growth.

ELIMINATION

Getting rid of what the body doesn't need takes almost as much energy as growing new cells. Lots of what we eat doesn't get used and we eliminate it through our bowels. Various toxins get eliminated through processes associated with production of urine, sweat, hair and nails. Look closely at what comes out of your child's body.

Feces – "Poop" provides a surprisingly accurate window into the mysteries of what goes on inside the long tube that makes up our gastrointestinal system. Keep track of your child's "poop" and share your observations with your doctor.

Look for regular bowel movements, once or twice a day. Too frequent bowel movements, in toilet clogging proportions, may mean that your child cannot digest his food very well. Infrequent, hard, pellet-sized, grainy or painful bowel movements may mean your child did not get enough water or fiber in his diet.

Look for brown feces with the texture and solidity of a ripe banana. "Poop" smells, but if you think the smell has gotten worse – or if another experienced parent or caregiver comments on how "bad" your child's "poop" smells, let your doctor know about it. Foul smelling feces may indicate an overgrowth of "unhealthy" microorganisms. Digestive upsets happen to everyone from time to time, but if you see any of the above symptoms on a daily basis, let your doctor know about it.

Urine – Our kidneys filter wastes so efficiently that generally our urine leaves our bodies in a sterile condition (free of microorganisms). Kidneys need plenty of water to do that. Look for light yellow to clear urine with a slight scent of ammonia. Often urine changes color and odor based on what we have eaten. Occasional variations in color and smell, after eating foods like beets and asparagus, indicate that everything is working well. Dark, yellow urine with a strong odor indicates that we have not had enough water to drink. When this happens every day it means the body has to work very hard to get rid of waste products and that takes energy away from other bodily functions like thinking and maintaining health.

Sweat – We regulate our body temperature through sweat glands and this also provides the body with an opportunity to detoxify. Adults and older children in many cultures use regular sweat baths to maintain health. Young children and babies cannot regulate their body temperatures well enough to safely use a sweat bath, but they definitely benefit from "working up a sweat" in vigorous outdoor play. Look for clear, salty, relatively odorless sweat when it first comes out of the body.

Sweat provides an excellent medium for bacteria and so if sweat stays on our bodies for hours or days, it can pick up an unpleasant odor.

Hair and Nails – Practitioners using ancient healing traditions, such as those from India and China, rely on the state of a patient's nails and hair to help them arrive at a diagnosis and treatment. Some dangerous foreign toxins leave our bodies through the hair and nails. Heavy metals like lead can make their way out of the body through this route. Doctors may test hair and nails for dangerous chemicals. Anthropologists and archaeologists use hair found in burial sites to help them determine the diet of ancient peoples. Look for strong, springy hair and smooth, strong nails in your children. Dull, lifeless, brittle hair and spotted, ridged or brittle nails can indicate dietary deficiencies.

BRAIN FUNCTION

Our brains demand a lot of energy to keep our bodies organized and successfully making sense of the world around us. When our bodies do not get the nutrients they need to make enough energy for growth and elimination, the brain gets shortchanged and we begin to see problems with the way we react to the outside world (sensory processing), coordination of our muscles, emotional regulation, and our ability to learn and solve problems of everyday life.

Sensory Processing – Our brains rely on the body to provide information about the outside world through the senses of balance, touch, taste, smell, hearing and vision. Even relatively small nutritional deficiencies can affect the body's ability to perceive and interpret these sensations. When the brain gets insufficient information or misinformation from the body it cannot do its job of organization and we see a variety of problems.

Occupational therapists, as well as physical therapists and speech pathologists specializing in *sensory integration*, pay close attention to the way children respond to the world through their senses. They look at how children move, what they like (or don't like) to touch, and how they respond to smells and flavors. Therapists observe how children respond to lights, sounds, language and movement of objects in the environment (like toys). Look for curiosity and active exploration of the environment. Look for young children using their mouths as a primary means of exploration, with food, toys, and all the things you'd rather they didn't put in their mouths. When therapists see overly cautious children fearful about exploring the environment through movement, touch, taste, smell, vision and hearing they use *sensory integration* and other sensory processing treatment techniques to help remedy this situation.

Coordination – Our brains use the information they get from the senses to coordinate all the complex movements we make with our muscles. At birth, babies can generally coordinate breathing, sucking and swallowing a few mouthfuls without choking. They get even better with practice. Once children have some teeth, they add chewing to this complex sequence of movements. Children learn how to get food into their mouths (as opposed to their eyes, heads, and the freshly mopped floor). Eventually they learn how to cook, handle money and drive to the grocery store. All of these skills serve the body's need for nutrition, but first and foremost you need to make sure that your child can safely breathe, suck and swallow without choking.

Speech pathologists, occupational therapists and physical therapists specializing in feeding, know how to make sure your child coordinates this complex process. They may simply watch your child eat and drink. If a therapist has questions about what happens in the back of the throat during swallowing she may recommend a "swallow study" using a radioactive dye and a fluoroscope. Your doctor will need to be involved in this process by ordering the study and helping coordinate any treatment that follows it.

Choking sometimes scares children and often scares their parents and caregivers. When children get scared of eating they become extremely cautious about what they choose to put in their mouth. When adults react to choking in a way that scares the child, it can make a child even more fearful of eating.

Emotional Regulation – Current research indicates that every cell in our bodies serves in our overall emotional regulation, and that the brain acts as a central organizer of this information. Our brains communicate directly with all of our muscles, internal organs, skin, bones, blood and lymph fluid. Because nutrition affects every cell in our body – it affects our brain. Our brain uses energy to manage all of this organization.

Our brains run on glucose, a sugar molecule, so our bodies process the foods we eat into glucose to feed our brains. It can do this even faster when we eat sweets. Our bodies produce insulin to take "sugar" out of the blood and put it where it needs to go (for storage as fat or used for growth, elimination, brain function and body maintenance). Because the manufactured forms of cane, beet and corn sugars are relatively recent additions to the human diet, our bodies overestimate the need for insulin. As a result, our blood sugar drops too quickly and we feel tired, shaky and emotionally fragile. After the initial burst of energy we get from consuming sweets, our energy level depletes, and the brain asks for more energy. Our bodies quickly provide it by releasing adrenalin and cortisol (the "stress hormones") making us "hyper," cranky, and itching for a fight.

Eating more sweets soothes the crankiness and hunger for an hour or two at best and then the cycle starts again and continues for as long as one eats sweets. If your child has frequent melt-downs and craves sweets you may have to help your child get over this "addiction" by increasing the variety of healthy foods in his diet. You will see major positive changes in behavior once your child begins eating a healthier diet. While other nutrients also affect the brain and therefore behavior, simply reducing the amount of sugar in our diets can lead to profound changes. A registered dietician or nutritionist who specializes in "biomedical interventions" and nutrition for children can help you deal with serious "sugar addictions" and other nutritional deficiencies.

Learning and Problem Solving – Our brains organize information from the senses in order to predict the world around us. We learn to predict what will happen from observation. Our brains need reliable information from the body and sensory organs. Many of these organs – our eyes, ears, nasal passages, tongue, skin, muscles, joints and bones – require a balance of nutrients in order to do their job. Food sensitivities, allergies and nutritional deficiencies all decrease our cells' ability to do whatever it is that they do best. Our brains depend on the right quantities of nutritional components to make useful observations of the world, and apply them in increasingly complex interactions. We call this learning and problem solving.

Look for children who enjoy exploring all aspects of the world through all of their senses. When children avoid foods they often avoid other forms of exploration as well. Children need exploration to predict what goes on around them and get what they need through learning how to navigate the world. If your child has trouble remembering, learning or exploring the world, eating a wider variety of foods may help him get the right nutrients to feed his brain. Feeling comfortable exploring the world with all of the senses – including taste, smell and the touch sensors in the lips and mouth – stimulates lots of brain cells and makes learning easier.

31

FREQUENTLY ASKED QUESTIONS

Q: I'm tired but my child seems like he could stay up 24 hours a day! Children always seem to have more energy than adults. If you work outside the home you will come home tired to a child who may have spent most of his day inside. He will need to run and play – just when you want to sit and stare at a TV for an hour. Find daycare and school settings that provide one to two hours of outdoor or active play every day or find local playgrounds and parks where your children can play hard with other children while you sit on a bench and watch. Active play can help your child eat and sleep better.

> **Have Fun** – Bring a sense of curiosity to the individual health factors that might affect your child's food choices
>
> **Play Safely** – Ask for help if you "feel" your child needs it.
>
> **Make Friends** – Play with your child every day.
>
> **Use Imagination** – Think about what your child "feels" before during and after meals.

BIOMEDICAL RESOURCES

What's Eating Your Child? The Hidden Connections between Food And Childhood Ailments: Anxiety, Recurrent Ear Infections, Stomachaches, Picky Eating, Rashes, ADHD, And More by Kelli Dorfman. (2011). New York: Workman Publishing. A comprehensive look at all ways food can affect children's behavior with practical suggestions for parents.

Sensational Kids: Hope and Help for Children with Sensory Processing Disorder by Lucy Miller and Diane Fuller. (2007). Perigee Trade. Full of insights about how children organize information about the world using their senses.

www.asdpuzzle.com – website for Elizabeth Strickland, nutritionist. She has articles and offers consultation services via phone.

MY KID EATS EVERYTHING

BIOMEDICAL HEALTH ISSUES

Let's explore some factors that could cause your child to become a picky eater.
you ideas about how to approach adding new foods and whether you need to seek some

	What We Want to See	Causes for Concern

1) Individual
  a) Energy
    i) Movement
	Plenty of movement - crawling, walking, running, jumping, climbing – all day long	Limited movement – long periods sitting in front of a TV or video screen

ii) Sleep	8-10 hours of uninterrupted sleep on most nights.	Less than 8 hours/day – naps lasting more than a few hours/day – fitful nights
iii) Mood	Generally alert, curious & happy	Frequent moodiness, lack of interest in the world around them
iv) Eyes	Bright, shiny & curious	Dull, listless, lids at half-mast.
b) Growth	Following a normal growth curve on a growth chart	Growth on the upper or lower curves of the chart
c) Elimination i) Feces	Brown, consistency of a banana, 1-2 times/day	Frequent constipation, yellow or grainy stool, 1-2 times/week
ii) Urine	Usually clear or light yellow	Usually dark yellow
iii) Sweat	Clear, salty, after active play or getting hot	Rarely sweats even when warm or after playing hard
iv) Hair & Nails	Smooth, hard, clear	Ridged, brittle, spotted
d) Brain Function i) Sensory Processing	Eagerly explores environment with mouth, nose, fingers	Avoids many textures, flavors, smells, sounds
ii) Coordination	Chews, crawls, walks, runs, jumps, climbs, catches & kicks balls	Often chokes, clumsy, awkward or slow to learn new movements
iii) Emotional Regulation	Generally happy and curious	Frequent "melt-downs"
iv) Learning/Problem Solving	Explores & figures out how toys work , enjoys school	Frequently asks for help figuring out new toys, dislikes school

CHECKLIST
Understanding why your child avoids foods will give outside professional help.

Get Professional Help Now	Primary Provider	Nutritionist	Therapy -OT	Therapy -SLP	Behaviorist	Therapy -PT
Rarely if ever moving – difficulty crawling, walking, running, jumping, or climbing	X	X	X			X
Inability to sleep more than a few hours at a time	X	X	X		X	
Generally unhappy, fearful or disinterested in the environment	X	X	X		X	
Dark circles under eyes, sunken eyes, unresponsive to movement or lights	X	X				
Weight loss, slowing down or lack of growth						
Frequent diarrhea, painful stool, large quantity, black, foul smell, 3-4 times/day	X	X				
Dark brown, red, orange, foul smell	X	X				
Frequently sweats even when not active or in cool temperatures, foul smell	X	X				
Thick, broken, opaque	X					
Avoids any unfamiliar movement, textures, flavors, smells, sounds, or changes in environment	X		X			
Frequently chokes, spits up, avoids movement	X		X	X		X
Generally unhappy, listless, or violent tantrums	X		X		X	
Prefers the same toys, avoids new experiences, "hates" school	X		X	X	X	X

SUSAN L. ROBERTS

CHAPTER FOUR

Re-Invent Traditions – Socio-Cultural Factors Affecting Mealtimes

Mary, a delicate seven-year old with finicky eating habits and fastidious hygiene, went on an overnight camping experience with her Girl Scout troop. Her father packed a special bag with wet wipes and the crackers and liquid yogurt drink Mary ate exclusively. Somewhere in the excitement of setting up tents and fishing for trout the bag got lost and no one remembered it – even Mary. The girls and their leaders sat around the campfire for a meal of pan-fried trout with milkweed leaves and dandelion greens wilted in bacon fat. For dessert they ate sticky toasted marshmallows in a sandwich of graham crackers and chocolate.

When the troop got home and Dad unpacked Mary's backpack he found the bag of food crushed under a dirty sweatshirt and wet bathing suit. He called the troop leader to find out what had happened and listened dumbfounded to how Mary caught, cleaned, and ate a trout. Even more surprising, he learned Mary ate her first green vegetables, common garden weeds. The troop leader explained that he had seen this happen on many camping expeditions and attributed it to the novelty of the experience and the appetite children develop after a day of active play outdoors.

Picky eating usually originates with unpleasant experiences in the way our bodies respond to what we eat, but mealtimes also reflect our relationships with family members, communities and our evolution as a species in a complex ecosystem. When problems with eating arise we want to examine some of these issues as well.

FAMILY

Mealtimes offer us a time to develop and maintain essential social relationships. Our first social bond occurs during our first "family meal" as mother brings a newborn to her breast. If the infant has difficulty "latching on," maternal anxiety rises and that anxious feeling gets communicated to the infant through "mirror neurons," (cells in the brain that become activated when we perceive those around us experiencing life). We call them "mirror neurons" because we have learned from brain imaging that the same parts of observers' brains "light up" when they watch others perform a task. Mirror neurons play a big role in learning, especially social and emotional learning.

New mothers feel more anxiety about breastfeeding than experienced mothers. When new mothers get assistance and helpful advice about breastfeeding their anxiety gets replaced with feelings of success and comfort. Sometimes difficulties with mealtimes begin during these first few meals. Even if a mother has no difficulty with breastfeeding, some infants still develop into picky eaters – for any of the reasons we outlined in the last chapter.

Eating Together – We learn what and how to eat from the people around us. If our family members and friends have certain preferences we usually adopt them. The journey from picky eating to adventurous eating has to involve the whole family. If your family does not eat any meals together now, you will need to get creative and begin thinking of fun ways to share meals as a family even once a month or once a week. Picnics, barbecues, Sunday brunch, or Saturday pizza parties could provide a starting place. Eventually you will want to share meals every day, but it might take some time to get that established, so go at a pace that feels comfortable for you and your family.

Exploring Together – Once you have established regular times to eat together you can use that time for "exploration" of new and unfamiliar foods. Perhaps everyone else in the family already likes to try new foods. Great! You will share the adventure of trying unfamiliar foods with your "picky eater" on this journey. If everyone in the family has reservations about trying unfamiliar foods that will work, too. You will all get more comfortable trusting your food exploration skills and in the course of learning these you will teach your picky eater how to trust her body, senses and self-control.

38

Processed foods, restaurant chains, and multinational agriculture industries have greatly reduced the variety of foods we consume. A thousand years ago we did not worry about what to eat; we ate what we could get and that changed with the seasons. We could find leafy green vegetables in the spring, fruits and berries in the summer. Autumn brought more fruits, squashes and root vegetables. In winter, we had to rely on grains and root vegetables flavored with fats and oils. Meats, fish and poultry also had seasons. Eggs and dairy products depended on the animals breeding cycle. Some of the joys of travelling involved sampling local specialties, like wild blueberries and lobsters in Maine, or mangos, bananas, and coconuts in Florida. Nowadays we can get all of these foods year round. If you live in Alaska and decide to live on nothing but mangoes and bananas, you can do it (if you can afford it).

COMMUNITY

The social bonds we make in families get extended through shared mealtimes. Uncle Bob's barbecue sauce becomes a town specialty. Variations on the recipe travel with the people who want to taste that dish again, whether they know Uncle Bob or even his home town. Often recipes came with a story. The stories become legends, ways of remembering our history. We often use these recipes and tell these stories at holiday meals.

Ritual Meals[4] – Holidays and ritual meals serve as a spiritual link between us, our ancestors and even our understanding of Life. Thanksgiving turkey, cornbread and pumpkin pie belong to the story Americans tell each other about the first European settlers who came to this continent. Passover *matzos* commemorate a journey from Egypt to the "promised land," when there was no time for fermenting (i.e., leavening) flours to make breads. Easter, combines the memory of Jesus eating a Passover *Seder* dinner with his disciples with various foods, such as colored eggs, that come from indigenous "pagan" traditions of the Mediterranean. *Iftar*, the meal Muslims share at the end of daily Ramadan fasting begins with three dates, to remind them of how the prophet Mohammed broke his fast. Hindus prepare and give away

---

4   By "ritual" I mean any repetitive set of utensils, ingredients or behaviors associated with food preparation or eating. These repetitive aspects of meals may have origins in maintaining health or as a means of conveying history and moral values from generation to generation. These behaviors tend to repeat over generations whether people remember the original reasons or not.

sweets during *Diwali*, the Festival of Lights. Sharing special foods and holiday meals connects us to our childhoods and to our ancestors.

Parties – More spontaneous "feasts" and "festivals" help us make new relationships. We invite neighbors over for barbecues, classmates to birthday parties, travelers and tourists to the "church supper" or "fireman's breakfast." Meals provide us with ways to share new foods and build new relationships. It turns out that our digestive systems usually thrive on this kind of variety. If they do not, it may indicate that we have restricted our diet in unhealthy ways.

Holiday meals and parties become extremely stressful for families with picky eaters. As your picky eaters get more comfortable trying unfamiliar foods at home they will develop skills for politely trying new foods. Chapter Ten helps you make holiday meals and parties more fun for everyone. Re-establishing these "food networks" helps your picky eater keep traveling on the journey to adventurous eating.

SPECIES

Homo sapiens co-evolved alongside other life-forms sharing this planet. We eat some of these life forms – plants, animals and fungi. Other life forms eat us. We rarely worry about ending up as lunch for a wolf or tiger, but our bodies host a complex ecosystem of microorganisms that help us digest the foods we eat. Some of these organisms do so by "eating" us.

Our gastrointestinal system forms an ecosystem that stretches from our mouths to our anus. The microorganisms that live in it serve us by converting foreign matter from the environment into useful components. Usually we think of these components as nutrients – substances that our body converts into energy for growth and maintenance. Microorganisms also convert potentially harmful substances into components that our bodies can eliminate. Some microorganisms in our GI tract actually spend time digesting us (parasites) and a good many microorganisms produce potentially harmful toxins that create more work for our bodies. Eliminating these toxins can use up tremendous amounts of energy – almost as much as the energy we need to grow new cells.

We like to think of these microorganisms as "good guys" and "bad guys" but sometimes we have trouble differentiating between the two. A little of one microorganism may help us digest food, whereas a lot of it may contribute to a food sensitivity. We get sick, our GI tracts get inflamed and we don't have the energy we need to grow, think and thrive.

Our first "inoculation" of microorganisms happens as we travel through the birth canal. Healthy, well-nourished mothers pass the "right" microorganisms on to their children. These organisms help the infant digest familiar foods for their culture. In places where parents don't have access to processed "baby food" or blenders, adults and older children chew food to pass on to babies, another way of sharing microorganisms. Healthy, well-nourished communities pass on beneficial microorganisms. Viral and bacterial "diseases" can get passed on as well. Individuals have immune systems that neutralize these threats, or not. Those with insufficient immune systems get sick and even die. Babies, young children, and the elderly have immune systems most susceptible to these threats.

Traditional Foods – Most non-industrial cultures have special foods they reserve for pregnant women, nursing mothers, children and the elderly. These special foods usually have more nutritional value and boost the immune systems of those who need it most.

Fermented foods – Before people had access to fire, let alone refrigeration, they learned that some plants and animal products tasted better if they sat around a while. They also learned that foods that had fermented lasted longer before going "bad". Milk products that sit at room temperature turn into yogurt, *kefir*, and cheese – depending on what organisms land in the milk. Our ancestors learned how to manipulate these microorganisms to make the best tasting foods. Those "healthy" microorganisms joined the ecosystem in our GI tracts and over time became an essential part of our immune systems.

Our ancestors also learned that grains, beans and seeds that soaked in water or other liquids, tasted better and caused less stomach distress. Some creative geniuses figured out how to make all sorts of "sourdough" breads by cooking these soaked grains, seeds and beans.

People have had the capability to ferment foods for tens of thousands of years. In that time the microorganisms in our GI tract evolved into a complex ecosystem that allowed us to digest and eliminate a fantastic array of plants, animals and fungi. For the past century we drastically reduced the variety in our diets and eradicated as many microorganisms as we could find. Our immune systems could not keep up with these rapid changes and many of our chronic diseases reflect these extreme changes in diet.

Slow food preparation – Traditional foods required preparation over days, weeks, months and sometimes years. We have learned how to replicate some of these dishes using high heat, microwaves, and other processes that make it easy to prepare similar looking foods in a matter of minutes. Usually flavor gets sacrificed for appearance and often essential nutrients get destroyed as well. It looks like we are eating food, but these "food-like substances" contain few if any of the vitamins, minerals and other nutrients our bodies require. Eating a steady diet of "processed foods," as we have done for three generations or more, has changed our digestive systems and possibly even our genes.

Our brains run on glucose, a sugar, so our bodies quickly process the sugars we eat and feed them to our brain. For roughly three million years the only way we got to eat large quantities of sweets was to find ripe fruits or wild beehives where we could get honey. Otherwise we got all our sugars through fresh milk, fruit, vegetables and cooked grains. About 10,000 years ago we figured out how to grow fruits, vegetables and grains. We also learned how to befriend and "domesticate" dairy animals and bees. Our bodies managed to change over this relatively brief evolutionary period. With the advent of modern food manufacturing over the past fifty or one hundred years, an onslaught of new "foods" have entered our grocery stores and found their way to our tables and our stomachs. We eat ever increasing quantities of processed foods with ever decreasing nutrients. Many chronic "modern" diseases reflect these rapid dietary changes.

Nutrient density – Traditional diets process plants, animals and fungi with fermentation and relatively low heat sources which preserve the vitamins, minerals, and other nutrients that get destroyed by high heat (pasteurization), microwaves, and radiation. The majority of foods we find in our grocery stores have undergone some or all of these processes, changing flavors and reducing the nutritional quality of everything we eat.

Most non-industrial cultures reserve their most nutritious foods for mothers, children and the elderly whereas we serve the most processed and least expensive foods in our schools, hospitals and nursing homes. We began doing this several hundred years ago in western "civilized" cultures. I believe we see the result of this trend in our picky eaters, many of whom also suffer from the current national epidemics of obesity, learning disability and autism.

Outdoor Play – If you have ever spent a day hiking, working in the yard or, sunbathing and swimming at the beach, you know that playing outside develops an appetite. Food eaten on these days tastes better. Your picky eater needs to play outside every day. It will help her develop an appetite. Current research indicates that sun exposure increases vitamin D, so if your child plays in the sunshine she will get that added benefit.

Before we had our current pharmaceutical arsenal, people with diseases like tuberculosis got sent to places like Arizona for fresh air and sunshine. Many of them got better. It took time and we get more consistent results with modern drugs, but I believe science will find out that fresh air and sunshine does us more good than simply increasing vitamin D as a supplement. This journey needs to include increasing the amount of time your picky eater plays outdoors.

Active Play – Children played outside a whole lot more fifty years ago than they do now. Mothers bundled their children in snowsuits or rain gear and shoved them out the door for a few minutes of uninterrupted peace and quiet in the house. Children built forts and tree-houses and developed complex rules for games and getting along with one another. We have more cars, more roads, fewer parks and very little open countryside available for today's children. Recess time has dwindled because of academic demands in spite of studies that show grades improve with more unstructured outdoor play time. Special needs children may get no outdoor play at all.

Contact with Dirt – Recent research seems to show that the presence of parasites (the ones who eat us) in our GI tract corresponds to a remarkable decrease in the occurrence of chronic inflammatory diseases like arthritis, Parkinson's, Alzheimer's and autism. A few doctors have begun treating these disorders with oral inoculations of parasites. Most parents I've met think "worms" are too "icky" to even contemplate. I agree. However, since we are talking about outdoor play, it occurs to me that crawling around in grass and dirt, climbing trees and making mud pies all seem like likely places to "pick up" these creatures.

No child should crawl and play around in sewage, subway platforms, or other "filthy" breeding grounds for dangerous microorganisms. Children need regular baths, shampoo, clean laundry, and frequent hand washing (with soap not antibacterial "goo"). Well-maintained parks and playgrounds probably provide children with plenty of opportunities to "challenge" their immune systems and current research shows that these "challenges" actually serve to strengthen immune responses and keep our immune systems from "attacking" us and causing chronic inflammatory diseases. Perhaps we could relax some of our vigilance and fears of what my mother always called "clean dirt".

Now that we have looked at all the issues affecting the way our bodies process food, I hope that you have a clearer idea of how your child found her way to picky eating. If you learned that your child needs professional help I hope you have gotten that process underway.

Let's take the next step on our journey – finding out what foods your child really wants to eat.

FREQUENTLY ASKED QUESTIONS

Q: How can I get more traditional foods into my child's diet?

I could not include recipes in this book so I have included lots of resources with recipes. This chapter includes a website for the Weston A. Price organization which has lots of information and links to recipes for traditional foods. Other chapters will have more resources. Many of these traditional foods, like baked beans, taste good at first bite, others, like sauerkraut, usually take time to appreciate. Take a look at the website. Try some recipes if you enjoy cooking. For now, just consider some of the possibilities. You may find out your family already eats some of these "traditional" foods. Remember you have just started this journey and give yourself and your child plenty of time with familiar foods before trying something new.

Q: I barely have time to microwave a TV dinner – let alone spend time playing outside with my child. How can I do this?

Have Fun – Play outside with your child every day that weather permits.

Play Safely – Consider socio-cultural explanations that might affect your child's food choices.

Make Friends – Read stories about food to your child, for instance, the *Hungry Caterpillar* and *Stone Soup.*

Use Imagination – Think of creative ways to get you, your child and the rest of the family to share some food

Take a look at your schedule and your neighborhood. Find a playground or open space close to routes you usually drive – most schools have playgrounds attached. Adjust your schedule to take fifteen minutes of time for parking the car and letting your child explore the playground. Bring a ball, some cars or a pail and shovel. You might only need to sit and watch your child play with other children or you might need to take a more active role in outdoor play. Have fun. The fresh air will do you both good – and much cheaper than a gym membership!

RESOURCES FOR EXPLORING SOCIO-CUTURAL ISSUES
Last Child in the Woods: Saving Our Children from Nature-Deficit Disorder by Richard Louv. (2008). Chapel Hill, NC: Algonquin Books of Chapel Hill. Documents how much outdoor play time children have lost; what research says about the benefits of outdoor play; and creative ways communities have acted to increase outdoor play for children.

In Defense of Food: An Eater's Manifesto by Michael Pollan. (2009). New York: Penguin. An insightful look at what we eat from a journalist who has traveled the globe exploring food.

www.westonaprice.org – website based on nutritional information derived from population studies done by Weston A. Price, DDS, begun in the 1930s. The site also provides access to recipes and other websites about traditional foods and food sources.

SOCIO-CULTURAL ISSUES HEALTH

Let's explore some factors that could cause your child to become a picky eater.
you ideas about how to approach adding new foods and whether you need to seek some

	What We Want to See	Causes for Concern
1) Family a) Eating together	Enjoy family meals every day	Share family meals less than once a week
b) Exploring together	Enjoy trying something new once or twice a month	Strict (not fun) rules for trying new foods, clearing plate
2) Community a) Ritual meals	Enjoy traditional holiday meals like Thanksgiving, Christmas, Passover, Ramadan, birthdays	Holiday meals often a source of friction rather than enjoyment
b) Parties	Enjoy getting together with family and friends for no particular reason	Rarely share meals with family or friends except special occasions
3) Species a) Traditional foods	Regularly eat meals made from recipes handed down through the family or from ethnic cookbooks.	Generally eat meals made with ingredients that ancestors would not recognize.
i) Fermented	Regularly eat foods with live probiotic cultures, like yogurt, homemade sauerkraut, pickles	Eat some yogurt, usually the sweetened kind
ii) Slow preparation	Meals cooked in a crockpot, roasted in an oven, or otherwise take 3-24 hours preparation	Meals cooked at home rarely take more than 30 minutes to make – including preparation
iii) Nutrient density	Using whole foods, including healthy fats, fruits & vegetables	Mostly packaged pre-prepared low-fat foods
b) Outdoor play i) Activity	1-2 hours/day spent in unstructured outdoor play in all but the worst weather	30 minutes or less a day unstructured play – only in perfect weather
ii) Contact with dirt	Regular contact with "clean" dirt like grass, sand, soil	Occasional contact with "clean" dirt – most often plays indoors or on pavement

CHECKLIST
Understanding why your child avoids foods will give
outside professional help.

Get Professional Help Now	Primary Provider	Nutritionist	Therapy -OT	Therapy -SLP	Behaviorist	Therapy-PT
Avoid family meals, everyone eats separately	X	X	X	X	X	
Everyone has individual dietary preferences & restrictions		X	X	X	X	
Avoid holiday meals whenever possible		X	X	X	X	
Avoid parties whenever possible		X	X	X	X	
All meals come from pre-prepared packages or restaurants		X				
Avoid yogurt or anything like it		X				
All food prepared in microwave or eaten in "fast food" restaurants		X				
Strict low-fat diet of packaged, pre-prepared foods	X	X				
Rarely, if ever, plays outdoors	X		X		X	X
Rarely, if ever, has made contact with grass, sand, soil	X		X		X	X

CHAPTER FIVE

What Does Your Child Really Want to Eat?

Four-year-old Harry's mother worked as a nurse in a pediatric unit at the local hospital, but she couldn't get him to eat anything the rest of the family ate. Finally she took him to a clinic that specialized in treating children's "feeding disorders." She explained that Harry refused to eat anything but cheese flavored corn puffs and liquid dietary supplements. The clinical staff planned to offer only "healthy" foods and insisted Harry would eat when he got hungry. After three days of no food at all, Harry collapsed and an ambulance rushed him to the emergency room.

Harry's mother began researching "picky eaters" online. She enrolled in several professional continuing education courses on treating childhood "feeding disorders" and eventually got a job in a clinic that worked with families struggling with mealtime issues. What she learned in these "child-centered" settings enabled her to come up with a program that worked for Harry. Within a year he ate almost all the foods she put on the table.

I imagine that your child's mealtimes feel more like a battleground than the loving, nurturing experience you want to share with him and remember about his childhood days. You have ideas about what foods taste good and which ones will help him grow strong and healthy. He insists, loudly, with all the drama and determination of a high priced defense attorney, that he will eat only the brightly colored marshmallow puff cereal. Please don't even mention milk.

You have already tried waiting it out – refusing to give him "junk" food – serving only "good" food – until you felt like a jailhouse guard in a bad movie about prisoners on a hunger strike. How many hours or days did it take before you gave in?

Learn from Harry's experience. Don't try the "starvation" technique at home. Often "problem feeders" don't ever feel hungry enough to eat a food they do not like. Problems with balance and movement may make a child (or adult) feel "motion sickness." Certain textures, smells, colors, or the sound of foods crunching in his mouth (or even someone else's mouth) may make him gag. Your child may have talent and a gift for drama, but these behaviors reflect what's going on inside his body – not a script in his head.

I'm going to ask you to do something really radical. For the next two weeks STOP caring about what your child eats. Approach your child as a scientist collecting data about a rare, endangered species. Get a crazy hat like your favorite scientist/adventurer wore in the latest movie. Wear your special hat during mealtimes to remind you that for this moment in time you are no longer "Mom." Print out the food journal forms and put them on a clipboard. Your child will recognize right away that "Mom" has changed the rules if she's wearing a funny hat and carrying a clipboard.

Observe VERY STRICT RULE #1 – "Have Fun!" and keep it playful during meals for the next two weeks while you collect data for the Food Journals.

Stop asking for your child to "take a bite" of something. Simply put a variety of food on the table – what you want to eat, what siblings want to eat and something you know your child likes to eat. Put a variety of food on the table even if only you and your child sit together at a table. Choose at least one food your child likes and some others he has never eaten. Avoid any foods that make him gag. Once you have put food on the table sit and eat what is on the table. Do not get up to add any new foods. If your child requests a particular food, not on the table, let him know you will serve that food at the next meal or snack. Let him get used to eating *what* you provide *when* you provide it, and *where* (sitting at the table).

Meals need structure. They need to have clear beginnings and endings. Some people say "grace" to start a meal. In some families people ask to be "excused" at the end of a meal. Use whatever rituals feel comfortable for you – begin doing them when you eat together with your child and then incorporate them into family meals. Eating together at a table will establish an important habit for helping your "picky eater."

Meals and snacks need to have assigned times during the day and these times need to remain as constant as you can make them. Our bodies do best when we can predict these rhythms. Everyone in your family may grab food throughout the day, but setting up special times and eating at a table instead of "on the go" turns out to be one of the best ways to establish healthy eating patterns. It will benefit every member of your family, not just your "picky eater."

Eat some of all the foods on the table. (You only need to take a small bite – just so your little one sees Mom eat everything.) Don't comment on the foods your child chooses. Don't even look directly at him while he's eating. Don't offer him a bite of anything on your plate. Put the food on the table and watch what your child chooses. Write it down in the Food Journal after the meal is over and your child has left the table.

Do this for at least one meal or snack a day. The first few days your child may eat ONLY the foods he usually eats. He may do this for the entire two weeks. That's OK. You are collecting data right now. You need to know where to start this process and what foods your child willingly accepts.

This technique comes highly recommended by Ellyn Satter – guru of children's nutrition and feeding dynamics. When I first started recommending it to families of "problem feeders" I used to worry that a child would only eat one food for two weeks and then stop eating it altogether – something we must avoid with "problem feeders" who cannot afford to lose a food. Instead of losing foods, families thanked me for two weeks reprieve from mealtime battles. Often they exclaimed that the child tried a food he had never eaten before. I relaxed about making the recommendation. Once again, we find that Ellyn Satter knows how to feed children.

WEEK NUMBER ONE

1) Print out "Food Journal – Nutrition" and use it for the first week.

2) Write down your child's name, your name and location (home, school, restaurant, etc.). Yes, I know you know your child's name, and no one else is keeping this log but you. Remember you are a scientist for this exercise and act "professionally." Besides, it will impress your doctor if you end up showing it to her.

3) Write down the dates you observe your child choosing foods.

4) Write down the foods your child eats.

5) Write down the portion of food based on your child's hand size. Our hands give a reliable portion amount based on our body size. Your hand reflects your correct portion and your child's hand reflects his portion. Start by giving your picky eater a portion size amount and let him eat as many portions as he wants – or let him serve himself in whatever quantity he likes. Most picky eaters get overwhelmed by too much food – avoid "super-sizing."
   a) Palm size equals a portion of protein – or other solid mass like pizza.
   b) Handful size equals a portion of carbohydrate – or scatter food like beans.
   c) The last digit of the thumb equals a portion of fat or sweets – like butter and jelly.

6) Keep track of the proteins, carbohydrates and fats your child eats. Nutritionists call these "macronutrients" and we need a balance of all three in our diets. Lots of foods contain two or three of these macronutrients so check each box based on your best guess about portion – use the same number for all three categories – if a food contains two or more macronutrients. A nutritionist might quibble about portions and categories but they will appreciate knowing exactly what your child eats and how much.
   a) Proteins – meats, poultry, fish, eggs, dairy, soy, beans. This group includes: the strange "meat/poultry" found in breaded nuggets from a fast food chain; hot dogs; cheese on your child's pizza or macaroni; a bottle of milk; liquid dietary supplements; peanut butter; and yogurt products.
   b) Carbohydrates – vegetables, fruits, grains, breads, pasta. This group includes: fruit juices; candy; cookies; crackers; "protein" bars; granola; canned spaghetti; macaroni and cheese; liquid dietary supplements; and pizza crust.
   c) Fats – oils, cream, nuts, butter, lard, other animal fats. This group includes: margarine and other "butter substitutes"; cheese[5]

on pizza and macaroni; peanut butter; liquid dietary supplements; whole milk; whole milk cheeses; and ice cream.

7) Make a judgment about the nutritional quality of what your child eats. If you know a nutritionist, ask their opinion about foods you question.

   a) Non-foods. These are substances none of us consider food. For instance, your child may prefer his paper napkin to steak. If you laughed, be grateful this is not your child. Obviously we do not want to let our children eat these non-foods, so don't serve dirt, laundry starch, or paint chips at the table, but do make a note of non-food items your child eats during the day. You need to figure out why your child wants to eat them.

   b) Sugar. If you don't know, check the food label. If you see sugar by any name (see Appendix A) in the top three ingredients on the label; or if the grams of sugar outnumber the grams of protein and fat in a serving size, then you're looking at a sugar – even if it says "heart-healthy," "organic," "protein-enriched," or "low-fat" in great big letters on the label.

   c) Processed food. If it has a label with more than five ingredients and you haven't seen one of those ingredients in the meat, dairy or produce aisles of your grocery store, it's probably a processed food.

   d) Whole food. Anything your grandmother or great-grandmother would recognize as food. Ask yourself, "Did George Washington eat this food?" If not, you can usually rate the food as a processed food.

WEEK NUMBER TWO

1) Print out "Food Journal – Sensory"

2) Write down your child's name, your name and location (home, school, restaurant, etc.). Yes, I know you did this already. Remember you are a scientist for this exercise and just do it.

3) Write down the dates you observe your child choosing foods.

---

[5] Real cheese actually contains all three macronutrients – proteins, fats and carbohydrates. Processed cheese may or may not have all components. You can find out by reading the nutritional label on the food product.

4) Write down the foods your child eats.

5) Write down the portion of food based on your child's hand size.
   a) Palm size equals a portion of protein – or a solid mass like pizza.
   b) Handful size equals a portion of carbohydrate – or scatter food like macaroni.
   c) The last digit of the thumb equals a portion of fat or sweets – like butter or jelly

6) Take a look at the sensory components that could affect your child's appetite and food preferences. The sensory aspects of food and mealtimes will help you figure out how to introduce new foods, and which ones to choose first (in Chapter Six). Put a "+" with a circle around it if the sensation stimulates your child (makes them more "hyper"). Put a "-" with a circle around it if it calms your child. You may not see the immediate results of calming or stimulation, but your child experiences it and chooses these sensory experiences as a way of regulating his nervous system.
   a) <u>Movement before a meal</u>. Children with "vestibular processing" problems usually seek out constant movement or avoid swinging, jumping, climbing, spinning, running and rolling. The "vestibular apparatus" in our inner ears sends information to all parts of our brains and bodies, so processing problems affect us in many different ways. Many children and adults with "vestibular processing" problems also have difficulties with balance and may even experience the nausea of "motion sickness" much of the time – a sure-fire reason to avoid eating. Observe your child's activity before a meal.
      i) *Stimulating* – Seeks out rapid movements, swinging, running, climbing, and spinning.
      ii) *Calming* – Slow rocking and rolling movements.
   b) <u>Textures</u>. How would you describe the food?
      i) *Stimulating* – Crunchy, hard, thick, gooey, hot or cold.
      ii) *Calming* – Gummy, soft, thin, silky, cool or lukewarm.
   c) <u>Smells</u>. What do you smell?
      i) *Stimulating* – Minty, citrusy like lemons, spicy like cinnamon, chemical like ammonia, acrid like coffee.

      ii) *Calming* – Fragrant like flowers, creamy like vanilla, soothing like cloves, herbal like basil or bergamot (the flavor in Earl Gray tea).

d) <u>Tastes</u>. If your child eats non-food items you may have to taste what he eats to understand what attracts him.

      i) *Stimulating* – Sour, bitter, spicy. We learn to like these flavors.

      ii) *Calming* – Sweet, salty, pungent. Our comfort foods – the flavors of mother's milk.

e) <u>Sounds</u>. What do you hear when you chew this food? What background sounds does your child like during mealtimes.

      i) *Stimulating* – Crunching, slurping, sucking, metal utensils on ceramic dishes, fast-erratic music (rock, rap, hip-hop, heavy metal), loud conversation or shouting.

      ii) *Calming* – Silent foods and utensils, slow and rhythmic music (classical, folk, country, rhythm and blues), soft conversation or no talking at all.

f) <u>Appearance</u>. Picky eaters get overwhelmed with too much food on a plate. Don't "supersize" their portions, but let them have as much as they want. How does the food look?

      i) *Stimulating* – Many bright colors, small shapes, bright, flickering lights or rapid movements, for instance, a video screen.

      ii) *Calming* – Monochromatic colors (usually white, yellow or beige), muted colors or pastels, large shapes, few details, slow movements, low and steady lighting

SUMMARY

1. For the next two weeks observe *Very Strict Rule #1* – HAVE FUN!
2. Pretend you are a scientist observing your child.
3. Print out "Food Journal – Nutrition" and use it the first week.
4. Print out "Food Journal – Sensory" and use it the second week.
5. Choose the same time and place to observe your child's meals every day. You may choose more than one meal and location per day, (e.g. at home for lunch, a restaurant for dinner.) Choose the times and places your family usually uses.
6. Put all food on the table at once.
7. Let your child see you eat a bite of each food on the table.

8. DO NOT indicate ANY interest in what your child chooses. It may be a few days before he notices you have "stopped paying attention."

9. Record and analyze foods AFTER the meal.

FREQUENTLY ASKED QUESTIONS

1. What if our family doesn't eat regular meals at consistent times? Everyone in your family will benefit from eating regular meals at consistent times. Start by scheduling one family meal or snack time each day with your picky eater and gradually add to this schedule. Your picky eater (and everyone else in the family) will do better if you: serve all meals and snacks at the table; provide meals and snacks at two-hour intervals; allow nothing but water between meals and snacks. Keeping such a schedule will ensure that your child feels hungry at mealtimes but doesn't feel "starved." Your child will also have an opportunity to learn how to eat new foods from watching parents and siblings eat them.

> **Have Fun** – STOP worrying about *whether* and *how much* your child eats for the next two weeks.
>
> **Play Safely** – Be curious about *what* your child eats *when* you put food *on the table*. Use the Food Journals to analyze his choices.
>
> **Make Friends** – Have fun at mealtimes – no matter what it takes
>
> **Use Imagination** – Put foods you know your child likes on the table, and add as much variety as you can imagine when choosing the foods you (and other family members) like to eat.

2. What if my child doesn't sit at the table? Do what you can to keep your child eating at the table and keep track of how many minutes he spends at the table during a mealtime. Your child will do better eating at the table (even if he is standing and not sitting). This may take a while. Keep

track of time to measure improvements. Ask for help with this from a behaviorist, occupational therapist or speech and language pathologist.

3. What if my child chooses to eat only candy and cookies?
   Candy, cookies and sweets are "sometimes" foods. When you put them on the table along with all the other foods, make sure you serve them in appropriate portions: ONE handful portion is plenty. Most children eat a few non-sweets. If your child ONLY eats candy and cookies, make an appointment with a registered dietician as soon as possible. Reducing or eliminating candy, cookies and sweets means your child will be hungrier for more nutritious foods.

4. Is a "food journal" really necessary?
   Yes. The food journal will give you a starting point. Knowing what foods your child likes, which foods provide the most nourishment and why your child might prefer certain foods over others (sensory issues) will enable you to plan which "new" foods to introduce first.

RESOURCES FOR OBSERVING

The Yoga of Eating: Transcending Diets and Dogma to Nourish the Natural Self, by Charles Eisenstein. (2003). Washington, DC: New Trends Publishing. Letting go of expectations and enjoying the experience.

Women, Food and God: an Unexpected Path to Almost Everything, by Geneen Roth. (2010). New York: Scribner. How to pay attention and enjoy what we eat.

www.ellynsatter.com – Ellyn Satter's website. More information than you can imagine on all aspects of eating, relationships during mealtimes, and how to enjoy the food we eat.

Food Journal - Nutrition

Child's Name: _____

Recorder's Name: _____ Location: _____

Food Journal

Date	What Child Eats	Portion	Protein (meat, fish, poultry, eggs, dairy, soy, beans)	Carbohydrate (fruits, vegetables, grains, breads, pasta, cereals)	Fat (butter, nuts, cream, oils, lard, fats from fish, meat, poultry)	Nutritional Quality

Nutritional Quality: 0 = non-food; 1 = sugar; 2 = processed food; 3 = whole food

Child's Hand Portion /: protein = palm size; carbs = handful size; fats/sugars = distal thumb digit

Food Journal - Sensory

Child's Name: _____

Recorder's Name: _____ Location: _____

Date	What Child Eats	Portion	Nutritional Quality	Movement Before Eating	Texture	Smell	Taste	Sound	Appearance

Nutritional Quality: 0 = non-food; 1 = sugar; 2 = processed food; 3 = whole food

Child's Hand Portion /: protein = palm size; carbs = handful size; fats/sugars = distal thumb digit

Sensory Components: Stimulating (+); Calming (-); Neutral (blank)

59

CHAPTER SIX

What Do I Want My Child to Eat?

Five-year-old Chloe only ate fish shaped crackers and packets of ketchup from her favorite fast food restaurant. Whenever the family travelled to visit her grandparents they took along these foods. Chloe's grandfather prepared traditional Italian meals, that everyone loved, except Chloe. In fact, Chloe would gag if she had to sit at the table with other family members eating grandpa's wonderful dinners. Fortunately Chloe's family had to travel a whole day to visit her grandparents, so the family used this excuse to avoid family visits.

Chloe began attending a special program for "problem feeders" at a local clinic. She learned how to eat ketchup from lots of different fast food restaurants and crackers shaped like bunnies as well as fish. Then she learned to dip crackers in ketchup and later tomato sauce. Chloe started eating canned spaghetti and meatballs and eventually her father's version of grandpa's recipe. During the annual visit "home," Chloe ate grandpa's spaghetti and meatballs while tears rolled down his cheeks.

Now you know what your child really chooses to eat – from two weeks of "observation in the field" as an anthropologist might put it. A behaviorist would call this list of foods a "baseline." Whatever you want to call it, you have a list of foods that your child likes to eat.

61

Continue serving your child the foods she likes. Continue observing the foods she chooses. Be sure to add any new foods she tries to list of foods she likes. DO NOT comment on her food choices, either positively or negatively. Feel free to do a victory dance in the privacy of your bedroom and e-mail all of your living friends and relatives whenever she tries a new food. Hold on to your hope. Bring your *energy, excitement,* and *enthusiasm* to mealtimes. Ditch your expectations at the door.

When you serve your child's favorite foods along with a variety of other foods she becomes more comfortable seeing foods she doesn't like to eat and recognizes that she doesn't have to eat them. In this chapter you will plot a clear course from the foods she likes to the foods you want her to eat, by adding foods that only slightly challenge her "comfort zone".

What foods do you want your child to eat?

Look at the "Nutritional Quality" ratings of the foods your child enjoys. Does she eat any whole foods? Regard each of those choices as a gift. Whole foods provide your child with the nutrients she needs to survive and thrive. I call them "lifeline" foods. Rejoice in those foods and continue serving them. If your child is a "problem feeder," leave these foods alone. Do not take the risk of turning a child "off" to a "lifeline" food by changing it in any way.

We want to turn your child's "processed foods" and "sugars" into whole foods in the "Nutritional Quality" column as soon as we can. The "Chaining Map" helps you plan *how* to do this.

Print out "06f Chaining Map" on the accompanying CD. Write every one of your child's favorite "sugars" and "processed" foods in the large spaces on the left-hand side of the page. You will map where you plan to go to get from the foods your child likes to the foods you want her to eat. Do this by changing her foods, one sensory component at a time.

Brand Names

Many children only eat specific brands for a variety of reasons. Eating "brand name" foods gives your child a way to control consistency in the sensory components of a food. If your child has a gastrointestinal issue or food sensitivity, she may have learned that these "brand name" foods feel better than other foods.

"Brand name" foods have multi-sensory components. Obviously the "branding" of product packaging gives it visual recognition, but the proprietary recipes of these products affect flavor, smell, texture, and even visual recognition outside of the package. You may not be able to discern any difference between chicken nuggets from *McDonalds* or *Burger King's* or between pureed carrots from *Beechnut* and *Gerber*, but your child can. Isn't that amazing!

Don't try to fool your child by putting foods in "non-brand" packaging. Sometimes confusion about a food's "predictability" will cause a child to stop eating that food altogether, a real danger with "problem feeders." Let your child know where foods come from and how you are changing them. Have her help you in the kitchen or make adjustments at the table. Give her permission to refuse a food until she gets used to the changes.

If your child likes "brand specific" foods the first change you make will be to introduce other brands. Look over your list. In the second column of "brand specific" foods write down three similar "brands" or variations within a specific "brand". In the "Sample Chaining Map" I have shown you how to do this with *McDonalds' Chicken McNuggets*, *Goldfish* crackers, and *Skittles*.

VISUALS

Apart from packaging, your child pays attention to the color and visual texture of foods. We all eat visually. Gourmet chefs and managers of expensive restaurants know this. If you spend a hundred dollars on a meal, you will get the correct portion of food. It will come to you on a large white plate. The foods will not touch each other and most likely the plate will have a colorful squiggle of pureed fruit and a flower. Make time to arrange foods artfully on a plate and see how your picky eater responds.

Often children with gastrointestinal issues find a food color that feels "safe" to them. They have learned from experience that many foods feel uncomfortable in their mouth, throat or stomach. Cautious children may go on a "white," "beige," or "yellow" diet to accommodate food sensitivities. If you have a child on a monochromatic diet, ask your doctor or other health professional to help you investigate the reason she chooses these foods.

You will need to introduce color slowly to a child on a monochromatic diet. On the "Sample Chaining Map" the "liquid dietary supplement" chain specifically works on introducing color, so that will give you an idea how to proceed. The ketchup and *Skittles* chains work with color and so do the other chains on the sample map.

TEXTURES

Many children respond negatively to textures in their foods. Multi-textured foods like yogurt with granola or pureed foods with some chunky pieces in them may be difficult for a child who has trouble coordinating breathing with sucking, swallowing, and chewing. Some children like the stimulation of crunchy foods but soft foods make them gag. They have their reasons for preferring textures, and you may enlist the help of an occupational therapist or speech and language pathologist to try to figure this out. For now, look at the sensory food journal. Which textures does your child seem to prefer. As you introduce "new" foods, stay with the textures she prefers.

Gradual and subtle changes in texture occur with the chicken nuggets and *Skittles*. More drastic changes occur with the other foods, but they happen gradually over time.

SOUNDS

Sometimes a child responds to textures of foods because of the sounds they make while she is chewing. Look for this if your child prefers crunchy and gritty or chewy and gummy foods. Listen to foods as you chew them and see if you can figure out whether your child is responding to texture or sound. Choose how you "chain" to "new" foods based on sound as well as texture.

FLAVORS

Most processed foods have overwhelmingly sweet or salty flavoring. As soon as you move from processed to homemade foods you gain control over the amount of sweetening and salt you add to foods. Be sure to add enough sweeteners and salt to foods to make that first transition from processed to homemade a subtle rather than a drastic one. Rest assured that the manufacturer will always add more sweetener and salt to processed foods than you could ever imagine adding in your kitchen. Taste the processed foods. Taste your homemade foods. Slowly reduce the amount of sweetener and salt in homemade foods until you arrive at the lowest amount that pleases your family.

Some children crave strong sour, bitter, spicy, or pungent flavors. If your child seemed to like these flavors on the sensory food journal, forget about bland-flavored, "kid-friendly" menus. Look for strong flavors like sour pickles, salsa, horseradish, pesto, balsamic vinegar and mustard. Remember you can always add salt, sweetener, and many other flavors at the table with spices and condiments.

SMELLS

Our sense of smell can detect even minute differences in chemical content of the air we breathe. Our sense of smell connects directly with the parts of our brain that house memory and emotion. Aroma therapy uses these connections to produce global changes in our bodies' response to the environment. Your child probably has strong feelings and memories about the smell of certain foods. You may be able to figure out where these originated, or not. If certain foods make your child gag, it will be more challenging to add them to her diet. Avoid serving foods that make your child gag until you have a FUN strategy for changing your child's response to these foods. You will learn how to do that in the next chapter.

NON-FOODS

If your child eats paper, dirt, paint chips, or any other "non-food" you face a different kind of problem. Get a nutritionist to help you figure out if your child has a nutrient deficiency causing her to make these strange choices. You will need to have your child tested by a doctor to determine if she has eaten enough of these "non-foods" to reach toxic levels of chemicals in her body. Paint chips pose a serious hazard because many paints contain lead which can cause brain damage and even death. Lead tastes sweet so children sometimes like eating it. If your child eats paint, take them to your doctor and ask to have lead levels checked. Get your house tested for lead paint and either move or find out how to prevent your child from eating more paint. Usually removing chipped paint and painting over lead paints with several coats of acrylic paint can prevent problems in homes with little or no lead paint.

You will have to analyze why your child likes "non-foods" better than "real" foods. You may have to put a little of what they eat in your own mouth to determine flavor or texture. Then try to find foods that recreate those flavors and textures. *Nori* seaweed, the kind used in sushi, has a texture similar to paper so you can see if your child will try eating *Nori*. Dirt eaters might be tempted by finely chopped mushrooms (they turn black when exposed to air). Add in some dry grits, cream of wheat or *Grape Nuts*® to give a "sandy" texture to the finely chopped mushrooms. If your child likes to eat seaweed and mushrooms you will have transitioned them from a non-food "0" to a whole food "3" in one step!

TRANSITIONING FROM SUGARS AND PROCESSED FOODS TO WHOLE FOODS

You want to get your child eating healthy foods as soon as possible. Getting away from "brand name food" and into homemade food allows you to take control and move your child from sugary and processed to whole foods.

Plain hummus, made from sesame paste and ground chickpeas (also called garbanzo beans) has roughly the same nutritional profile as peanut butter with a milder flavor and less stickiness. It usually has no sugar added, unlike many "brand name" peanut butters. Look for it in the dairy section of your supermarket. If your child likes it you can try all the different flavors.

Pureed fruits and vegetables (or baby foods) add color and flavor without adding texture. Some pureed fruits, like mashed banana, even provide enough sweetness to leave out other sweeteners. Add jellies, pureed fruits or even canned pie fillings to yogurt by the spoonful until you reach a flavor point your child likes. You will always add fewer sweeteners than the manufacturer.

Dips make wonderful transition foods. Your child can lick a favorite dip, like ketchup, off a "new" food or put a favorite food into a "new" dip. Make quick and healthy dips from yogurt or sour cream and dried soup mixes. Turn dips into sauces and put them over noodles as a variation on macaroni and cheese. Do the same to rice, bread or meats to add another level of variety into your child's diet.

FREQUENTLY ASKED QUESTIONs

1. My child gets tube feedings and refuses to put anything in her mouth. How do I get her to eat?

    If your child has a feeding tube you will need to work closely with your "feeding team" – your doctor, occupational therapist, speech and language pathologist, and behaviorist. Make sure they all talk to each other about how to help you do this. Give them a copy of this book if necessary.

    Before children eat, they learn to explore the world with their mouths. Most children with feeding tubes have experienced trauma to the nose, mouth and throat through medical procedures prior to and while putting the feeding tube in place. Your child may not remember these events, but her body carries the memory and it makes her cautious or fearful of having any foreign objects around her mouth. You will need to work with your child and her therapists in order to get over these aversions. You will get more ideas for doing this in Chapter 9: Having Fun With Food.

    > **Have Fun** – Arrange small amounts of food on plates. Give foods crazy names like "razzle dazzle raspberries" or "captain crunchy celery."
    >
    > **Play Safely** – Use the chaining map to plot out ways to move from sweets to wholesome foods.
    >
    > **Make Friends** – Relax the nutrition rules for now and keep eating together. Avoid any foods that make your child gag.
    >
    > **Use Imagination** – Think about which sensory aspects of foods your child finds most appealing. Use these maps as guides, be ready to adjust the plan as your child chooses "new" foods.

2. My child gags, screams, cries or flat out refuses to eat whenever I bring a "new" food to the table. How do I get him to actually try something different?

   Avoid those foods that make your child gag, scream, or cry, for now. Pay no attention to refusals. Your child gets to decide **whether** and **how much** she will eat. You will learn a FUN game for trying "new" foods in the next two chapters.

RESOURCES FOR CHOOSING FOODS

Food Chaining: The Proven 6-Step Plan to Stop Picky Eating, Solve Feeding Problems, and Expand Your Child's Diet by Cheri Fraker, Mark Fishbein, Sibyl Cox, and Lucy Walbert. (2007). Da Kapo Press. How to plan simple one step changes in a child's favorite foods so they can progress to more variety in their diet.

Secrets of Feeding a Healthy Family: How to Eat, How to Raise Good Eaters, How to Cook, 2nd Edition by Ellyn Satter. (2008). Madison, WI: Kelcy Press. One of many books by this author. It pretty much covers everything.

www.autismtreatment.org – the website for Son-Rise – chock full of wonderful information and tips that will help all parents, especially those whose children have special needs.

Favorite Foods	Alternatives 1	Alternatives 2
McDonalds Chicken McNuggets®	*Burger King®* chicken nuggets	frozen chicken nuggets
	Wendy® chicken nuggets	nuggets without breading
	other "fast food" nuggets	alternate protein nuggets
Goldfish® crackers	*Annie's®* cheesy bunnies	crackers dipped in cheese sauce
	Alternate flavor *Goldfish®*	crackers dipped in onion dip
	cheese flavored crackers	crackers dipped in hummus
Skittles®	*Starburst®* candies	sweetened dried apricots
	Life Saver® chewy fruits	candied cherries
	other chewy fruit flavored candy	candied kiwi or lime rinds
Liquid Diet Supplement (LDS) *(Check with MD or RD before modifying)*	LDS with applesauce	LDS with carrots
	LDS with pureed pears	LDS with peas
	LDS with mashed potatoes	LDS with beets
Sweetened Yogurts	same texture/different brand	plain yogurt, add flavors
	change flavors/same brand	
	same flavor/different texture	
Ketchup	try different brands	red mild barbecue sauce
		red sweet & sour sauce
		red spaghetti sauce

Sample
to Get There

Alternatives 3	Alternatives 4
homemade nuggets	nuggets dipped in ketchup
homemade chicken circles	nuggets dipped in hummus
homemade protein circles	nuggets dipped in gravy
veggies dipped in cheese sauce	vegetable cheese casserole
veggies dipped in onion dip	bread spread with onion dip
veggies dipped in hummus	toast with hummus
sweetened papaya	fresh papaya, apricot, cherries
dried cranberries	frozen corn or baby peas
fresh kiwi	red & green peppers cut into small pieces & frozen
pureed carrots	carrots with texture
pureed peas	bread dipped in peas
pureed beets	beets mixed with hummus
dip crackers in yogurt	mix yogurt with rice
dip cereals in yogurt	mix yogurt with cereal
dip fruit in yogurt	mix yogurt with fruit
dip meats in sauces	barbecue sauce on meats
dip tofu in sauces	sweet & sour stir frys
dip noodles in sauces	pasta with red sauces

CHAPTER SEVEN

The "First This, Then That" Game

Six-year-old Matthew did not speak and had trouble walking. He avoided all kinds of food except for the familiar breaded chicken pieces from his favorite fast food restaurant, accompanied by sodas and French fries with ketchup. His mother worried about the fact that he ate no fruits and vegetables. Matthew's pediatrician told his mother that Matthew needed to cut back on the "junk food" because he had gained too much weight for his age and height. When Matthew's mother tried giving him breaded chicken at home he gagged. When she let him go hungry for a few days, he ate nothing and he had multiple tantrums.

Matthew's mother had no idea how to help him take the next step for eating new foods until she read Cheri Fraker's book Food Chaining. She eagerly showed the book to her son's behavioral therapist and together they devised a "first this, then that" game. Matthew's mother started by holding out a nugget from another fast food chain with her left hand and one from his favorite in her right hand. She said, "first this," indicating the chicken in her left hand, "then that," indicating the chicken in her right hand. She placed the chicken in her left hand closer to Matthew so he had to push it out of the way to get the chicken in her right hand. Over the next few months Matthew and his mother played the game at every meal. Matthew had to do more and more with the "first this" foods to get to the "then that" foods. They had fun playing the game and slowly Matthew began eating new foods.

Up to now you have made no comments about *whether* or *how much* food your child eats. Now you will need to teach your child how to interact with the new foods he has avoided. The "first this, then that" game makes it easier to progress through your child's food chain and begin exploring new foods together as a family. Even if your initial progress seems immeasurably slow, once your child realizes he can go at his own *pace*[6] he will "try" unfamiliar foods more readily.

Print out the "Food Progression Chart" from the accompanying CD and write down all the foods you want to try based on the "Food Chaining Map." Introducing one food over and over gets boring so vary the "first this" foods. Use the "Food Progression" chart to keep track of how many times and in which ways your child "tried" a "new" food.

Print out a passport so your child can have fun keeping track of his own progress if you think he will enjoy doing so. Make this game LOTS OF FUN! Even if your child doesn't understand or enjoy the passport, he can still follow the progression sequence and play the "game." Have patience.

Make the game REALLY *exciting*. Show LOTS of *enthusiasm*. Yes, it will take plenty of *energy* on your part, but some day, usually before starting college, your child will eat broccoli without any prompting from you. Can you go to the trouble of "putting on party clothes" once a day for that?

Start with a regularly scheduled snack time, preferably a snack time when you can give your picky eater a lot of attention. Sometimes siblings can help with the game, and sometimes a picky eater needs your full attention. You will know which works best for your child by trying out both scenarios.

Most people take about twenty repetitions of a new food before they learn to like it. Of course, all of us have foods we've tried a million times and still don't like. The "Food Progression Chart" lets you keep count of how many times your picky eater actually tries a new food and whether he learns to like that "new" food.

Look at the sequence[7] of "trying" new foods on the "Food Progression Chart."

---

6   Marsha Dunn Klein, occupational therapist and mealtime expert says, "adults set the goals, children set the pace." You will find a video and her website in the list of resources for this chapter.

7   I owe many of the steps in this sequence to one developed by Kay

Fido's Dish – If your child gags even looking at a new food you must start by getting him to tolerate that food in the same room. Have your child "feed" a new food to the "dog" under the table, in the room, or even down the hall if necessary. You might have to do this first to show your child what you mean. Go ahead and act SILLY. Remember, you are playing a game. This first step sets the stage for the steps that follow it. You need to reassure your child that he can experience a new food at his own *pace*. Make it easier by acting silly and having fun.

If you have a dog, they LOVE this game. If you don't already have a dog that eats "people" food, go out and buy a stuffed dog and a special dish you can carry in your purse. Put the dish (and dog) under the table, or across the room, or down the hall – whatever distance your child can tolerate for the first session. Move the dish closer with each session until your child gets comfortable putting a "new" food into a dish under or next to the table.

Mikey's Plate - Who is Mikey? In the 1960's *Life* cereal had a commercial promoting *Life* (considered an adult cereal) to children. In the commercial several boys, about eight or nine years old, decided to "try" the cereal by giving it to Mikey, about five, first. "Let Mikey try it," said one of the boys, "he eats EVERYTHING!" Mikey tried it, liked it and the rest of the boys poured themselves a bowl.

Once your child has gotten comfortable feeding a new food to the dog, have him put the new food on "Mikey's plate." Maybe you know a real life "Mikey." If so use that name. You could call it "Santa's plate," "grandma's plate," or even give the food to another member of the family at the same table. Establish a habit of passing off new foods to someone's plate whether that person is present or absent, fictional or real. Each interaction with a new food brings a higher level of comfort.

Hide the food – We all did this as kids in my family. Mom put a serving of something "yucky" on our plate and we mashed it flat with our fork. Then we scraped it up into a narrow pile. Then we carved out a little "bite hole." As soon as she looked the other way we pushed some of it under the lettuce and a little more under the mashed potatoes.

Toomey, PhD, psychologist and feeding expert. Her Sequential Oral Sensory (SOS) Approach to Feeding has helped countless therapists, children and families. Dr. Toomey works at the Star Center in Colorado – www.starcenter.us.

Sometimes we got "caught" but more often Mom just kept looking the other way. Teach your picky eater this "survival skill" and encourage him to use it. "Hiding food" works much more successfully than screaming, crying, choking, gagging, or spitting in public eating establishments. Your child will learn to "hide food" as a survival skill during holiday dinners in Chapter Eleven, "Surviving Holiday Meals."

Touch the food – Skin to food contact introduces texture into your child's experience of a new food. He has already had to deal with smelling and seeing a food during the first two steps. Touching brings the food into "intimate" contact and can be VERY *exciting* (the positive spin on challenging). Give him some encouragement and space to do this on his own terms. Accept even brief contact at first and count with your child to increase contact time. Celebrate every second.

Move food closer to the face – Intimacy increases as we move food closer to the mouth. Simply picking up a food increases the contact time. Touching food to an elbow, shoulder or cheek increases the *excitement* level. Stay calm and reassuring during this phase. Give encouragement and praise lavishly.

Smell the food – Up to this point, a child with good breath control can hold his breath to avoid or minimize smelling the food. Now we are asking him to deliberately take in that aroma. WOW! How does it smell? Does it smell like something else you remember? How does that smell make you feel? Where do you feel it – in your head, tummy, chest, throat or somewhere else? Questions distract and provide a way of processing high voltage emotions (i.e. *excitement*).

Smells enter our brain via a single neuron so they make direct contact with nerves that hold memories, gastrointestinal responses, and emotions, for everyone. Smells can easily overwhelm your picky eater so use your *energy, enthusiasm* and *excitement* to help him take this big step with food. Let him know that sometimes we feel smells in our tummy or throat and it's OK to gag a little bit until we get used to these new smells.

If a smell reminds you of a memory from a time you and your picky eater had a challenging time (like a pediatric intensive care unit or a stressful family dinner) talk about that memory and smell. He may not have words to describe that experience or feeling, but you do. Talk about it to help him process the emotions his body remembers. He may associate smells with experiences you have not shared and about which you have no knowledge. If he has words, he might describe these experiences to you. If not, understand that memories associated with negative feelings affect our food choices. Honor his feelings and keep playing the game so he gets a chance to associate positive feelings with these smells.

Kiss the food – Our lips have as many nerve endings as our fingers so texture will play a role in "kissing" a food. As food gets closer to the mouth *excitement* mounts. Stay calm and use praise and encouragement lavishly.

Lick the food – Just like lips and fingertips, our tongues have lots of nerve endings that process texture. In addition our tongues have taste buds. Ask your picky eater if the food tastes salty, sweet, sour, bitter, or like something else. We can taste all flavors everywhere on our tongue in spite of what you might have learned in grade school about "taste zones." Use these questions as a distraction and a way to help him feel in control of this *exciting* new experience.

Spit the food into a napkin – Here comes another "survival skill" for picky eaters. Getting a food out of the mouth and quietly hidden in a napkin has saved many of us from having to swallow a food we realized did not "feel good" in our mouths. You will have to teach "spitting" and "spitting into a napkin" with foods or objects your picky eater finds acceptable before you get to this point in food progression.

Practice spitting as far away from the table as you can get. Even better, have a non-related adult (like your child's occupational or speech therapist) teach this "forbidden" skill "secretly." You do not want any random spitting going on at mealtimes. You do want children who can control food well enough to spit it into a napkin and you can only get there through practice, especially if your child has difficulty with "oral-motor skills," that is, coordinating sipping, chewing, breathing and swallowing. Spitting, although gross, appeals to children, and works marvelously well to develop oral-motor skills for the lips and tongue. If you arrange for your child's therapist to "secretly" teach these skills, you can ask your child to spit into a napkin (once he knows how) and still say, "I don't care what you do in therapy, there will be NO SPITTING going on at this table," if he spits chewed up food into his plate or across the table. For more ideas about spitting games see Chapter Ten, "Having Fun with Food."

Bite the food – Biting is code for "chewing." At first your child will probably bite the food with the front teeth and avoid letting the food travel too far back in his mouth. Eventually, as the food softens, it will travel backwards and biting will begin to involve the molars. You will keep encouraging your child to see how many times he can "bite" a "new" food. After about 25 "bites" the food will disintegrate to a point where it slides down the throat. On that day pull the tickets to Disneyland out of their hiding place!

Swallow the food – The day a bite of a "new" food slides down your picky eater's throat is a day for celebration. Share your *excitement* and *enthusiasm* about this tremendous step he has taken. Put a gold star on the passport next to the food you have written down. Buy tickets to a movie. Bring out the toy he has "lusted" after for weeks. Stand on your head. Do a dance. CELEBRATE!

You may have to run through this entire sequence for many "new" foods until your picky eater understands all the steps, trusts that you won't make him go too far too fast, and learns to have fun with the "first this, then that" game. Once he trusts you and himself, the game becomes more fun. Soon he will start to skip steps on his own. Believe it. Hallelujah!

Whenever you get ready to serve one of your picky eater's favorite snacks, make a small portion of a food from the next column on the "Food Chaining Map." Let your picky eater know that they can have the food they like, *after* they "try" the "new" food first. *"First try this, then you can have that."*

For example, if your child only eats chicken nuggets from McDonalds, you have to get her to eat chicken nuggets from any fast food chain. Each one has variations in smell, flavor, texture and taste. Perhaps you can't distinguish any differences, but your child can tell the difference. Go to the other fast food chains and purchase an order of chicken nuggets. Put them in plastic bags, label the bags with what's in it, where it came from and a date. Then freeze the nuggets and save the packaging. One order will probably take you through the entire food "trying" progression.

Buy an order of nuggets from McDonalds and bring them home. Take ONE chicken nugget from the freezer. Thaw it in a microwave or toaster oven. Cut the previously frozen nugget into three or four pieces and put it in its original packaging. Bring both packages to the table. Tell your child, "FIRST let's TRY THIS by feeding it to the dog, THEN YOU CAN HAVE a McDonald's nugget." Repeat as often as you have pieces and as long as you're having fun.

NEVER try to fool a picky eater by "hiding" a food they don't like. Usually it won't work, and if it does and he finds out you have "tricked" him you will lose his "trust." This food progression creates trust in the adult-child relationship and builds on that trust. KEEP YOUR CHILD'S TRUST foremost in the "first this, then that" game.

If you plan to eat your snack at a restaurant, put ONE frozen chicken nugget (or whatever) in a plastic bag. Most processed foods have enough preservatives to keep even "fresh" processed foods at room temperature for an hour or so without any ill effects. Most likely your child will not get the "new" food anywhere close to his mouth for the first half dozen times you try this so do not worry about a frozen food "going bad."

Trying new foods in a restaurant may require bringing in "outside" food, which violates some public health regulations affecting restaurants. Try not to get caught. If someone from the restaurant objects, explain that you need to use the "outside" food as "therapy" for a "special needs" child. Let them know how much your child LOVES their brand, which is why you eat in their restaurant so often. Hopefully this will work. You might find out that having a stuffed "purse dog" allows you to play the game more easily in a restaurant.

Keep track of the new foods your child tries by using the "Food Progression" chart. This way you can pick different foods every day and not lose track of where you are. Give each "new" food at least three tries before moving to the next highest level. Sometimes you can move several levels in one snack session. Sometimes you need to repeat a level for several different snack times. Let your child *set the pace*. If you keep having fun, eventually your child will get used to "new" foods and even learn to like some of them.

FREQUENTLY ASKED QUESTIONS

Q: My child eats breaded chicken from only one fast-food restaurant. Do I really need to go through all these steps with other brands?

Yes. Even though you do not see a difference, your child does. Honoring his experience will build trust and teach him the sequence in a "safe" way. Learning the sequence with something as similar as different brands of the same food makes it easier to do this with more "different" foods.

Q: I got my child to feed new foods to the dog and even to put them on Mikey's plate but he refuses to put a "new" food on his own plate.

Try creating an extra step whenever your child gets stuck. You could use a "try" bowl and place it closer and closer to your child's plate. He could even "touch" the food in the "try" bowl with a utensil and his fingers before moving on to "hiding" the new food on his plate. As a parent you need to figure out how to make each "next" step successful. Be creative.

Q: My child can chew up a food into a liquid and still spit it into a napkin. I do not think he will ever swallow it.

He might not, but he is fully experiencing the food and "trying" it. Give up expecting him to swallow it and move on to more foods. Be sure to celebrate the day he does finally swallow a new food.

Q: How long should I stay at one step?

Stay on each step as long as your child needs to stay there. Keep encouraging your child but give up expecting him to move forward. As Marsha Dunn Klein, occupational therapist and mealtime specialist says, "adults set the goals, children set the pace."

Have Fun – Act silly and have fun with the "dog" and "Mikey."

Play Safely – Institute the "first this – then you can have what you want" habit. Keep track of foods your child has tried.

Make Friends – Move at your child's comfort level. Remember hold onto hope, let the expectations go and keep up the *energy*, *enthusiasm* and *excitement*.

Use Imagination – If your child gets "stuck" on a level, figure out an "easier" step. Do whatever it takes to help your child be successful progressing with food in a playful, fun way.

CHILD CENTERED RESOURCES
The 'Get Permission' Approach to Mealtime and Oral Motor Treatment by Marsha Dunn Klein. (2003) Tucson, AZ:

Mealtime Notions. This video shows parents and professionals how to get a child's permission to move forward at mealtimes.

www.mealtimenotions.com – Mealtime Notions - Products and information from Marsha Dunn Klein, occupational therapist and mealtime expert.

www.popsiclecenter.org – Parent Organized Partnerships Supporting Infants and Children Learning to Eat – a source for stories, information and support.

"Courtesy Bite" - Food

Food Item	Fido's dish			Elijah's plate			Explore with utensil			Explore with fingers		

d Progression

Move toward face			Smell up close			Kiss the food			Lick the food			Spit the food			Bite the food			Swallow the food

83

CHAPTER EIGHT

Menu Planning: The Advantages of Eating Together

Six-year-old Emma only ate chicken soup with star-shaped noodles and peanut butter and jelly sandwiches. Her teenage sister followed one "fad" diet after another. Their mother cooked a meal for the adults and a separate meal for each child without complaining for years until her husband got diagnosed with diabetes. At that point Emma's mother refused to cook four meals and told Emma's father he would have to do all the meal planning and preparation.

Emma's father, an engineer and retired military officer, approached his new duties with the thoroughness he brought to all his work. He researched nutrition to learn how to cook for diabetes. Then he read Ellyn Satter's book, *The Secrets of Feeding a Healthy Family* and began following her rules for preparing family meals. He cooked foods he needed to eat, but always included a dessert or side dish the rest of the family liked, even if he could not eat it. No more separate meals, no more raiding the refrigerator after dinner. At first he listened to a lot of complaints and watched in silence as his children ate dessert first, and sometimes exclusively. First his wife, then his teenage daughter, and finally even Emma began trying the unfamiliar "diabetic-friendly" foods. Mealtime conversations began to revolve around subjects other than food. His shining moment came when Emma's friend said, "I wish my family had dinner together like this."

Eating together as a family will do more to help your picky eater than anything else. This means regularly scheduled meals, served at a table, free of outside distractions such as the television, phone calls, and texting. Like most modern American families, you may find this difficult. Often other family members balk at the idea of taking time away from "more important" tasks. Because eating meals together plays such an important role in the journey from picky eating to adventurous eating, I want to spend this chapter on rationales, strategies and resources that will help you make family meals possible.

Planning and beginning to prepare meals on a scheduled plan will take enormous effort on the part of the "chief cook and bottle washer." If you work outside your home I highly recommend taking a week off of work so that you can devote the kind of time this next step deserves. Eating family meals will benefit your family right now. Eating healthy foods together will enable your children to grow into healthy adults. You could find no better way to spend your time.

If mealtimes have become a battleground in your house, DO NOT start another skirmish over sitting at the table and turning off the cell phones. Find what Buddhists call "the middle way," a peaceful transition to family mealtimes. If you have followed the VERY STRICT RULES up to this point you have figured out how to share at least one FUN meal or snack a day with your picky eater. Hopefully some other family members have joined you. In this chapter you will prepare your family for sharing meals together.

Our species evolved into the current era of technological marvels and instantaneous worldwide communication through sharing food cooperatively, sharing meals, sharing conversation, and sharing love. Old fashioned "Darwinism" aside, we did not arrive at this state of "civilization" through "survival of the fittest." Or rather, we did, but "fittest" (even to Darwin) meant those best suited to cooperation, not murder and mayhem. Contemporary evolutionary biologists, anthropologists and social psychologists all agree that cooperative skills prepare us individually, socially, nationally and as a species for survival. Survival begins with preparing and sharing food.

It turns out that eating together as a family at mealtimes also helps with maintaining a healthy weight, reducing stress, preventing teen pregnancy and drug use, reducing the risk of cardiac disease, academic improvement and business success. Did I mention that food changes everything?

You may not view your role of "chief cook and bottle washer" as very privileged and powerful right now, but I hope by the end of this chapter you will begin to see how much influence you have to change your family's life for the better.

So how do you get your family to eat together?

You have spent the last few weeks learning what your picky eater likes to eat. Now check in with the rest of the family. Print out the "Favorite Family Foods" form on the CD. Fill out what you like first, and then spend some time individually with each member of the family. Tell them you plan on making more family "sit down" meals. Let them know you want to make sure to include ALL of their favorite foods. Ask them what they like to eat best in every category. Just listen to their answers without making comments or judgments, positive or negative. Put on your "party clothes," stay in the moment and remember to keep it FUN.

At the start of family meals you will relax the nutritional rules – or throw them out altogether, just as you did with your picky eater. Your goal: get as much acceptance as possible before beginning, but stay in charge. As "chief cook and bottle washer" you get to be the boss of *what* to serve for meals, *when* to serve them and *where* to eat. Take your power and embrace it.

The following descriptions might help family members think about *what* they like:

PROTEINS AND FATS

Meats – beef, pork, lamb – could include hamburgers, steak, bacon, sausage, hot dogs, pepperoni pizza, and gyros.

Poultry - chicken, turkey, quail – could include chicken nuggets, turkey sausage, chicken hot dogs.

Fish – and shellfish – could include fish sticks, tuna salad, fried clams, clam chowder and lobster.

Beans and nuts – a great source of inexpensive protein – could include baked beans, peanut butter, almonds, peanuts, walnuts, hummus, black-eyed peas, refried beans, soy beans, and tofu.

Eggs and dairy – a source of protein and healthy fats – could include milk, yogurt, omelets, quiche, whipped cream, butter, and cheeses of all kinds.

CARBOHYDRATES
Vegetables – canned, frozen and fresh – could include green beans, peas, carrots, celery, lettuce, sweet potatoes, spinach, kale, corn, beets, beet tops, broccoli, and all sorts of seasonal vegetables.

Fruits – canned, frozen, fresh and dried – could include apples, oranges, bananas, grapes, raisins, dried cranberries, and strawberries, and all kinds of seasonal fruits.

Breads – grains and other starches – could include white, wheat, rye or raisin breads, rice, spaghetti, pizza, muffins, rolls, crackers, and potatoes.

Sweets – "sometimes foods" – could include candy, cookies, cake, ice cream, granola bars, pie, milkshakes and ice cream floats.

Beverages – other than water – could include juice, sports drinks, carbonated soft drinks, herbal teas, cocoa, tea and coffee for the grownups.

Get lots of ideas from family members for foods they like. Look at examples of the "Small" and "Big Meal Menus". I tried to list foods your family probably already eats – even if you are getting lots of meals out at fast food restaurants. Fill out the "Small Meal Menu" form with ideas for snacks, lunches and small breakfasts. Fill out the "Big Meal Menu" form with meals your family enjoys for dinner or and big breakfasts. Some families have "breakfast for dinner." If your family might like that, give it a try.

You must also figure out *"when"* to serve meals.

Once you know what everyone likes to eat, make up some schedules and menus. When we do not take time to plan for meals and snacks, we tend to skip meals, grab "fast food" or "graze" all day long. You will need to serve meals and snacks at consistent times – for everyone's safety and comfort levels.

Each of these meals or snacks needs a starting point and an ending point. Meals need to last 20-45 minutes and snacks need to last 10-20 minutes. Why? Structured meals provide your child with some major benefits:

The two-hour interval between meals and snacks gives your child's body a chance to regulate her blood sugar, an essential component of brain and body function. Your child's body needs to learn how to regulate blood sugar so she can manage her emotional responses to the environment and learn.

The two-hour interval gives your child a chance to experience a feeling of hunger, but not one of starvation or deprivation. We eat when we feel hungry. We eat too much when we feel "starved."

Children need consistency and the ability to predict what happens in their lives. Consistent starting and ending points provide a predictable schedule. If you maintain a schedule it won't take long before your child learns to eat at the table because that's where her hunger for food gets satisfied.

Serving food at a table on a consistent schedule gives you, the "chief cook and bottle washer", control over the *what, when* and *where* of meals and snacks. That falls within your responsibilities. Your child has to decide *whether* and *how much* to eat. You must learn to trust your child's instincts about *whether* and *how much*. The unpleasant result of not trusting your child often becomes "force feeding." Don't let this happen.

MAKE A REALISTIC MEAL PLAN

Think about how your family operates right now.   Answer the following questions for your family.

What time do you, and your family members, get up most days?

Do you eat breakfast?

How much time do you ("chief cook and bottle washer") have to prepare meals and snacks before heading off to work?

Does your picky eater currently take a mid-morning break when she could eat a snack? (the British call this "elevenses"). Children need a snack at mid-morning. Find out if your child's school provides this time. If not, find a way of introducing it into her schedule. (See the FAQs at the end of the chapter.)

What time do your children have lunch?

Do they bring lunch to school or buy a "hot" lunch at school?

Does your picky eater actually eat anything at school all day?

What time do your children come home from school?

What kind of snack do they eat when they get home? An after-school snack might be the best time of day to introduce new foods. Why? Traditional Ayurvedic medicine (based on 5,000 years of experience) advises us to eat our biggest meal between the hours of 10:00 AM and 2:00 PM because our bodies digest foods most easily during that time of day. Many children eat very little at school and will come home hungry. TAKE ADVANTAGE of the wonderful opportunity that hunger + optimum digestive function offers for healthy snacking after school. In the United Kingdom they call this meal "tea" whether it includes a caffeinated beverage or not.

When does everyone get home from work or school?

How much time do you, REALISTICALLY, have to make a meal after work?

Do you sit down to dinner as a family? If so, when?

How much time do you have after dinner before getting ready for bedtimes?

Do you have time to prepare lunch and snacks at the end of the day?

Do your children eat "before bed" snacks?

How soon after snacking do your children go to bed?

Do you have more time to prepare for the next day's breakfast, lunch and snacks after the kids go to bed?

How does your schedule change on weekends and holidays?

Every family operates differently. As you read through the questions imagine what times might work best for your family.

Now, use the information from your "Menus" to fill out a "Mealtime Plan" on the form. Some of you will find it easier to plan ahead and then follow your plans. Other readers will do better filling in days as they go along. When you have successful days, where mealtimes go well, write them in the "Mealtime Plan." I have provided a sample mealtime plan based on my sample "big" and "small meal" menus.

If eating scheduled meals is new to your family, pick only one or two days a week to have a sit down" dinner. Make a game out of learning table manners. You can even dress up as a way to let family members know that these mealtimes have different rules than before. Make them a party! Put all the food, including dessert (only 1 portion of dessert per person – served individually NOT "family-style"). Share the following "rules" of mealtime behavior. For best results, make it a game.

Once the cook sits down, no more food gets added to the table. Eat what you like.

Pass food around the table and say, "Yes, please" if you want some.

If you don't want a food say, "No, thank-you."

It's OK to eat dessert first, and only eat dessert if that's all you want.

It's OK to take all the peas out of your casserole, if you don't like peas, but DO NOT talk about it and keep the peas on your plate (or in a separate optional "Fido's dish," "Mikey's plate" or "try" bowl).

Absolutely no whining allowed.

When you have finished eating – ask to be excused from the table. (Aim to keep everyone at the table for 15 minutes, longer if you can, or shorter if children get too restless.)

No raiding the refrigerator or food handouts until the next scheduled snack or meal. Keep the two-hour "fast" for optimal blood-sugar metabolism. Drink only water between meals.

FREQUENTLY ASKED QUESTIONS

Q: My child's school doesn't have any breaks during the day for snacks (or they eat lunch at 10:00 AM) and they refuse to let my child have a snack on her own. What can I do?

Make an appointment with your child's teacher and principal. Briefly describe your child's issues with food and mealtimes and ask for their help in making your suggestions work. Bring in no more than three suggestions and prepare to accept only one of them. (You can build on this later.) If the principal and teacher refuse to make any "accommodations" remind them, as gently as possible, that US Federal Law (Individuals with Disabilities Education Act "IDEA") requires that children with special needs get support in schools. You may need to schedule another meeting. In the meantime find other parents in your school, community or online to help you problem-solve ways to get "reasonable accommodations" for your child. This may require writing a legal document: an IEP (Individual Education Plan) or "504 Accommodation Plan." You may find school therapists, school nurses and other school staff very helpful – or not. You may need to get your family doctor to submit a letter or school form. Do research these topics online. Don't give up. Food changes everything.

Q: What if my child doesn't speak or can't understand about "manners"?

Children, even non-verbal or very young children, learn from watching others. If your child has siblings get them to help teach "manners" by demonstrating good manners themselves. Treat your child respectfully and politely. Get help from a therapist or behaviorist. As she gets older the "life skill" of table manners will ensure that your child gets included in school outings, family gatherings and other important community activities.

Q: My child has sports and other activities from the time school gets out until 8 PM so we cannot sit down to dinner as a family. What can we do?

When children have scheduled activities from the end of the school day until bedtime (or even later) family dinner often gets left by the wayside. Research shows that eating together as a family will have a positive impact on weight, health, and academic success as well as avoiding drug use and teen pregnancy. If you have enrolled your child in afterschool activities for any of the preceding reasons consider scaling back on these activities to allow time for family dinners. You will save money by eating together as a family and eating together as a family will help your child become a more adventurous eater. This means better nutrition and overall health. As "chief cook and bottle washer" you must make and enforce these decisions. Exercise your authority – it will help your family in the long run.

Q: My kitchen is such a mess I can't even find the sink and I'm storing sweaters in the oven. How can I possibly cook a meal at home? Get help and get help soon, for yourself, and especially for your children. Right now – check out _www.flylady.com_. This fabulous website will walk you through the

Have Fun – Enjoy sitting down to eat together. Include items that your picky-eater likes, even if it is fish shaped crackers.
Play Safely – Make a plan and follow it until you can put one week together. Continue until you have three weeks put together. No one will remember what they ate two-weeks ago .
Make Friends – Remember you choose the _what, when,_ and _where_ of meals. Your family members choose _whether_ to eat and _how much._ DO NOT comment on people's food choices. Feel free to comment on behavior and enforce the "manners game" rules.
Use Imagination – Avoid challenging anyone's food choices for now. You have spent a lot of time and effort to get your family to this point. Celebrate yourself!

clean-up process one "baby step" at a time. You'll start by "shining your sink." Marla will give you directions and you can watch an amusing and inspiring video on the website. This supportive website will reassure you that "you are not behind," and help you "jump in" wherever you are. Check it out!

Q: The family seems to "hate" sitting at the table. Everyone eats and leaves as soon as possible. I only get two syllables out of my teenager. I ask her about her day and all I get is "O-kay." How can I make mealtimes more fun?

Older children and adults often put up the most resistance to family mealtimes, whereas younger children usually love the added attention. Try"Table Topics for Kids" (*www.tabletopics.com*) and "Family Dinners" (*www.theboxgirls.com*) both offer collections of conversation starting questions. Put a card at each family member's place at the table. Go around the table reading the questions. Have everyone answer each question. Before you know it the gloomy teens start talking. Keep at it. One day they will proudly invite their friends over to show off these "fun" family dinners.

MENU PLANNING RESOURCES

Feeding the Whole Family: Recipes for Babies, Young Children, and Their Parents by Cynthia Lair. (2008). Seattle: Sasquatch Books. Great recipes for nutritious child-friendly meals.

Secrets of Feeding a Healthy Family: How to Eat, How to Raise Good Eaters, How to Cook, 2nd Edition by Ellyn Satter. (2008). Madison, WI: Kelcy Press. This book has information about nutrition, recipes and a meal plan already worked out for you.

www.savingdinner.com – Saving Dinner - menus, recipes & shopping lists for making simple dinners at home.

Favorite Foods of Each Family Member

	Chief Cook & Bottle Washer	Other Adult	
Meats			
Fish			
Beans/Nuts			
Eggs/Dairy			
Vegetables			
Fruits			
Breads			
Sweets			
Beverages			

Sample Small Meal Menus
Provide three or four per day

	Menu 1	Menu 2	Menu 3
Protein and Fat	Milk	Hard-boiled egg	Cheese stick
Carbohydrate	Cereal	Toast	Juice
Extra Fat (optional)		Butter	
	Menu 6	Menu 7	Menu 8
Protein and Fat	Tomato soup made with milk	Milk	Cheese dip
Carbohydrate	Crackers	Cookie	Corn chips
Extra Fat (optional)	Cream cheese		

Proteins and Fats = meat, poultry, fish, dairy, eggs, nuts, nut butters
Carbohydrates = fruits, vegetables, starches, sweets

Menu 4	Menu 5
Luncheon meat	Chicken soup
Bread	Noodles
Mayonnaise	

Menu 9	Menu 10
Peanut butter	Hummus
Apple slices	Celery

	Menu 1	Menu 2	Menu 3
Proteins & Fats (1/ meal)	Milk	Eggs & Bacon	Tuna casserole made with milk & canned soup
Grains or Starches (1-2/ meal)	Cereal Toast	Potatoes Toast	Noodles Bread
Fruit or Vegetable (2/meal)	Juice Fruit on cereal	Juice Tomato slices	Peas in casserole Canned beans Celery sticks
Fats (for flavor)	Use whole milk (under 2) Or 2 percent milk	Bacon	Butter
Sweets (optional)	Jam on toast	Honey on toast	Ice cream

Proteins and Fats = meat, poultry, fish, dairy, eggs, nuts, nut butters
Carbohydrates = fruits, vegetables, starches, sweets

Menu 4	Menu 5
Cheese on pizza (meat optional)	Chicken nuggets
Pizza crust Garlic sticks	Breading on nuggets Crackers
Tomato sauce Fruit slices	Carrot sticks Fruit slices
Cheese (does triple duty!)	Nuggets fried in oil (one fried food/meal)
Fruit slices (bring from home)	Soft drink

ACTIVITY/TIME	MONDAY	TUESDAY	WEDNESDAY
MORNING PREP 6:30 AM 15-30 minutes	Pack lunches & snacks, make toast	Pack lunches & snacks, put waffles in toaster	Pack snacks, take meatloaf out of freezer, make toast
BREAKFAST 7:00 AM 10:00 weekends	Milk, cereal, toast, juice, butter, jam	Milk, waffles, berries, butter, syrup	Milk, cereal, toast, juice, butter, jam
AM SNACK "Elevenses" 10:00 AM	Hard-boiled egg, juice	Cheese dip, corn chips	Yogurt & fruit
LUNCH Noon	Chicken salad sandwich	Granola bar & milk	School pizza
PM SNACK "Tea Time" 3:30 PM	Chicken noodle soup	Hard-boiled egg, toast, butter, jam	Peanut butter & fruit slices
DINNER PREP 5:30 PM 30-45 minutes	Cook rice, add left-over Sunday chicken, heat veggies, canned whip cream	Boil noodles, add soup, milk & peas to tuna, slice carrots, heat spinach	Heat meatloaf, mix instant potatoes, heat corn, cut fruit
DINNER 6:00 PM	Chicken and rice, carrots and peas, bread, butter, berries with whipped cream	Tuna casserole, carrot sticks, spinach, bread, butter, ice cream	Meatloaf, mashed potatoes, butter, corn, bread, fresh fruit salad
PM PREP 8:00 PM 15-30 minutes	Slice carrots, & celery, put in water in fridge	Slice fruit, put in salty water in fridge	Mash garlic into butter, spread on bread slices, refrigerate

© Susan L. Roberts, 2011

MEAL PLAN

THURSDAY	FRIDAY	SATURDAY	SUNDAY
Pack snacks, make toast	Pack lunches & snacks, take dogs out of freezer	Cook bacon, eggs, make toast, prepare & freeze meatloaf	9:00 pack snacks, get dressed for church
Hard-boiled egg, toast, butter, jam	Milk, cereal, toast, juice, butter, jam	Eggs, bacon, potatoes, toast, juice, fruit slices, butter, honey	Cereal, milk
Peanut butter, celery, raisins	Hummus, pita bread	Are you kidding? We just ate breakfast at 10!	Cheese stick, fruit slices
Corn dog	Peanut butter & jelly sandwich	Cheese dip & corn chips	Sausage, pancakes, toast, juice, fruit slices, butter, syrup
Milk, cereal, toast, juice, butter, jam	Tomato soup, crackers & cream cheese	Milk & cookies	Bean dip & celery
Boil noodles, add meatloaf to sauce, make salad, heat bread, cook berries for topping	Cook's night off or Heat dogs, &microwave popcorn	Cook's night off	Bake or buy chicken, mix potatoes & gravy, heat beans, cut fruit
Spaghetti with meat sauce, garlic bread, salad, ice cream with fruit topping	Movie Night Hot dogs, popcorn, carrot sticks, fruit slices, soda or water & candy	Pizza, salad, garlic sticks, fruit slices	Roast chicken, mashed potatoes, gravy, bread, green beans, fruit salad, ice cream
Hot dogs out of freezer, refrigerate sliced carrots & fruit	Take ground meat out of freezer	Take chicken out of freezer	Boil one dozen eggs, refrigerate

CHAPTER NINE

Getting the Whole Family to Try New Foods

Colin could hardly wait to go to kindergarten, but his mother had misgivings. Colin's teacher had a reputation for serving "strange" foods at snack time and she insisted that all the children try these strange foods. Colin's mother explained to Ms. Smith that Colin only ate veggie puffs, a sweetened yogurt with a colorful brand name cereal in it and a special brand of apple juice. Ms. Smith tried to reassure Colin's mother that all the children in her class learned how to try new foods and that Colin would do "just fine." Colin's mother dropped him off on the first day and returned home full of worry.

On the first week of school Ms. Smith brought in three "A" foods, animal crackers, apples and arugula (a spicy green leaf). At snack time she passed around the plate of arugula first. Ms. Smith encouraged all the children to "try" some. Most of the children just said "no, thank-you" and passed the plate to the next student. Colin gagged a little as he held the plate at arm's length and passed it to the boy next to him. Next, Ms. Smith passed around a plate of apple slices. Most of the children took one or two. Colin passed the plate with another suppressed gag. For the final course Ms. Smith passed around a big plate of animal crackers and all the children took a handful. Colin took one and had a small nibble, but he didn't eat it.

On the last week of school Ms. Smith brought in three "Z" foods for their final "feast," ziti with tomato sauce, zucchini and zabaione (an

Italian custard dessert). They started with dessert first, the zabaione, followed by zucchini and then the ziti. Colin took a big helping of all three and ate two whole slices of zucchini while his mother proudly watched. He had even begun trying "new" foods at home!

You will have the most success trying "new" foods when you do it as a family.

By now I hope your family eats together at home (or at a restaurant) three to five nights a week. Your children have gotten used to the idea that the "chief cook and bottle washer" doesn't care whether they eat or how much. I hope you have gotten used to serving at least one or two of your picky eater's acceptable foods at every meal. I hope that other family members have gotten to eat their favorite foods as well.

With luck your picky eater has started eating a few "new" foods already. If he eats a couple of "new" foods every week you probably don't even need the rest of this book. If you still feel frustrated by the food choices your picky eater makes (and maybe other family members as well), get ready to change things for the better.

Ask yourself. Does the family usually enjoy mealtimes? You want your family comfortable about family meals before embarking on the challenge of adventurous eating. Keep serving what family members like until mealtimes feel like FUN and everyone can sit at the table for fifteen or twenty minutes.

Your picky eater already knows the "first this, then that" game from snack time, but the rest of the family just eats their "favorite" foods during meals. Now, you will challenge your entire family to try a "new" food at least a couple of times a week. We want your picky eater to watch how everyone tries new foods, and learn from watching others having FUN trying new foods together.

Print up a "Passport" for every member of the family (including you). Hand them out. Let your picky eater help teach the "first this, then that" game to the rest of the family.

As "chief cook and bottle washer" you will have to do a bit more work planning meals, specifically, adding something new to the dinner menu, at least once or twice a week. I recommend relatively inexpensive and easy to prepare vegetables and grains. In the beginning, you may be throwing most of the "new foods" away, so choose things that don't cost much. Use vegetables in different preparations to give your family multiple opportunities to get used to a new food. Try expensive foods, like unfamiliar meats, at restaurants where you can order only one serving, preferably an appetizer or side dish. Pass this new food around the table. Let family members see how far they can go in their passport. Make it FUN!

Make sure all your children, especially your picky eater, see how much FUN you can have exploring new foods. Grown-ups need to make use of "Fido's dish" and "Mikey's plate" to let the children know that it's OK to say "not yet" to an unfamiliar food item. Many adults have had unpleasant experiences with food and may feel reluctant to start the "first this, then that" game, but adding more variety to our diets helps everyone's health.

With a little practice and permission to say, "not yet" your family can actually enjoy exploring new foods. You will find that some new foods taste great and get added to your menu. Everyone might want to avoid other foods. Not everyone will agree on all of the foods. Perfect! Now you have something to talk about and wonderful stories to tell friends and family.

My family used to go to a Chinese restaurant once a week in Washington, DC. My mother decided to try a "bitter melon" dish on the menu. Our waitress advised against it, but my mother insisted our family was "adventurous" eaters who liked "everything." Guess what? The waitress knew the dish better than we did. Every family member took one (and only one) bite and we all agreed, "never again." For years we entertained each other by telling the "bitter melon" story. Thirty years later I tried another preparation of bitter melon and found it quite tasty. I even grew the beautiful vine in my garden.

We always knew when my mother planned to sneak her "beloved" liver into our dinner because if we asked, "What's for dinner?" She always replied, "Something good." One night she used a recipe that tasted so badly, even she could only eat a few bites. Then we fed it to the dog and he refused to eat it. We laughed about that story for years. As children none of us ever ate more than one bite of liver. As adults we all like it and cook it at home.

Keep "trying" new foods in various preparations until every member of the family has gotten all the way to "swallowing" a bite of the new food. We call that a "courtesy" bite. If no one likes a "new" food by that time, cross it off your family's list. If some family members do like the new food, continue to serve it.

Remember, everyone eats only what they want to eat at a family meal. Follow these guidelines to keep peace and harmony – and to put an end to running a "short order" restaurant at your house.

The "chief cook and bottle washer" only prepares ONE balanced meal that includes a main dish, two side dishes, bread (or other everyday grain) and an optional dessert.

All foods (except desserts) go on the table "family style" so family members can decide whether to eat – and how much to eat.

Once the "chief cook and bottle washer" has put food on the table and sits down, NO more food gets added to the table. What you see, is what you get.

Desserts get served in single portions. No seconds allowed.

Absolutely no whining allowed. Eat it or not. No complaints accepted.

Encourage some form of "trying" a "new" food. Make it a game. Make it fun. Use "Fido's dish," "Mikey's plate" and the passports. Adults must play along with the children.

Adults can correct "table manners" but make NO comments about whether or how much family members eat.

FREQUENTLY ASKED QUESTIONS

Q: I barely manage to follow the menus I do have. How can I add new foods?

Look for an appealing "easy to cook" cookbook at the library or bookstore. I recommend <u>Glorious Greens</u> to families. The authors have simple preparations of lots of inexpensive leafy green vegetables. We could all use more leafy greens in our diets, and you will probably find some your family really enjoys.

Get on the mailing list for one of my favorite online resources: Saving Dinner (*www.savingdinner.com*). Leanne Ely sends lots of free tips and recipes. You can also subscribe to a weekly email with menu plans, recipes and a shopping list. Leanne also sells "bundles"- collections of menus for dishes you can freeze. These enable you to cook for a day and eat for a month.

Q: My child refuses to sit at the table even for a few minutes. How can I get him to sit with us at meals?

Have Fun – Use the passports and make it an adventure
Play Safely – Institute the "courtesy bite" rule once children have gotten comfortable trying new foods. Fall back on "Fido's dish" and "Mikey's plate" whenever necessary. Remember individuals get to decide *whether* and *how much* to eat.
Make Friends – Grownups and siblings play along during family meals.
Use Imagination – Introduce "new" and inexpensive vegetables, grains and breads to the whole family.

Start with snack time. Begin by only serving your child from the table. NEVER let your child take his food away from the table to eat it, but let him come back to the table for every bite if necessary. When your child gets used to coming to the table for food, get him to sit in a chair before giving him food. Once he's sitting in the chair, get him to stay longer by making it a game to ask for and receive food. When he can sit at the table for fifteen minutes, he's ready to join the family for meals. A behaviorist, occupational or speech therapist can help you succeed in getting your child to sit at the table for meals.

Q: My child gets fussy or misbehaves after he finishes eating. His whining makes the meal miserable for the rest of us. What should I do?

When a child starts whining, it's time for him to leave the table. You can keep him nearby with toys, but don't make him sit at the table after he has finished, especially if he makes the meal uncomfortable for others.

Q: My child leaves the table early and then wants another meal soon after we have finished eating. I'm worried he's not getting enough to eat. What should I do?

Stop giving your child "on demand" meals. He needs to learn that food gets served on a schedule and that he must join the family for meals. Once he learns that he gets to eat what he wants with the rest of the family food during meals he will join you. He may miss some meals and have a few tantrums along the way. If he misses an important meal, make sure he gets plenty to eat at his next snack to make up for it. Learning to share meals with others is a very important "life skill" that your child will need to thrive as an adult. Take the time and trouble to teach it now.

Q: My teenagers (or other adults) wonder why they cannot just make food they like and bring it to the table to join us, or heat up leftovers later?

Explain the importance of sharing food as a family: that it builds relationships and will help your picky eater learn to like unfamiliar foods. If that explanation does not work, fall back on "those are the rules."

CREATIVE RECIPE RESOURCES

Glorious Greens: More Than 140 Ways to Prepare All Those Great-Tasting, Super-Healthy, Beautiful Leafy Greens by Johanna Albi, and Catharine Walthers. (1996). New York: St. Martins Griffin. We could all use some more delicious and affordable leafy greens in our diets.

www.greensmoothiegirl.com - Information & recipes for kid-friendly vegetables & raw foods.

www.gnowfglins.com – God's Natural Organic Foods Grown Locally and in Season. Cooking courses, videos, information and recipes for simple and delicious traditionally prepared foods.

ACTIVITY/TIME	MONDAY	TUESDAY	WEDNESDAY
MORNING PREP 6:30 AM 15-30 minutes	Pack lunches & snacks, make toast	Pack lunches & snacks, put waffles in toaster	Pack snacks, take meatloaf out of freezer, make toast
BREAKFAST 7:00 AM 10:00 weekends	Milk, cereal, toast, juice, butter, jam	Milk, waffles, berries, butter, syrup	Milk, cereal, toast, juice, butter, jam
AM SNACK "Elevenses" 10:00 AM	Hard-boiled egg, juice	Cheese dip, corn chips	Yogurt & fruit
LUNCH Noon	Chicken salad sandwich	Granola bar & milk	School pizza
PM SNACK "Tea Time" 3:30 PM	Chicken noodle soup	Hard-boiled egg, toast, butter, jam	Peanut butter & fruit slices
DINNER PREP 5:30 PM 30-45 minutes	Cook rice, add left-over Sunday chicken, heat veggies, canned whipped cream	Boil noodles & potato, add soup, milk & peas to tuna, slice potato, heat spinach	Heat meatloaf, make quinoa, heat corn, cut fruit
DINNER 6:00 PM	Chicken and rice, carrots and kale, bread, butter, berries with whipped cream	Tuna casserole, sweet potato sticks, ranch dressing, spinach, bread, butter, ice cream	Meatloaf, quinoa, butter, corn, bread, fresh fruit salad
PM PREP 8:00 PM 15-30 minutes	Slice carrots, & celery, put in water in fridge	Slice fruit, put in salty water in fridge	Mash garlic into butter, spread on bread slices, refrigerate

© Susan L. Roberts, 2011

110

MEAL PLAN

THURSDAY	FRIDAY	SATURDAY	SUNDAY
Pack snacks, make toast	Pack lunches & snacks, take dogs out of freezer	Cook bacon, eggs, make toast, prepare & freeze meatloaf	9:00 pack snacks, get dressed for church
Hard-boiled egg, toast, butter, jam	Milk, cereal, toast, juice, butter, jam	Eggs, bacon, potatoes, toast, juice, fruit slices, butter, honey	Cereal, milk
Peanut butter, celery, raisins	Hummus, pita bread	Are you kidding? We just ate breakfast at 10!	Cheese stick, fruit slices
Corn dog	Peanut butter & jelly sandwich	Cheese dip & corn chips	Sausage, pancakes, toast, juice, fruit slices, butter, syrup
Milk, cereal, toast, juice, butter, jam	Tomato soup, crackers & cream cheese	Milk & cookies	Bean dip & celery
Boil noodles, add meatloaf to sauce, make salad, heat bread, cook berries for topping	Cook's night off or Heat dogs, slice fruit & microwave popcorn	Cook's night off	Bake or buy chicken, mix potatoes & gravy, heat kohlrabi, cut fruit
Spaghetti with meat sauce, garlic bread, arugula salad, ice cream with fruit topping	Movie Night Hot dogs, popcorn, carrot sticks, papaya slices, soda or water & candy	Pizza, eggplant, garlic sticks, fruit slices	Roast chicken, mashed potatoes, gravy, bread, kohlrabi, fruit salad, ice cream
Hot dogs out of freezer, refrigerate sliced carrots & fruit	Take ground meat out of freezer	Take chicken out of freezer	Boil one dozen eggs, refrigerate

SUSAN L. ROBERTS

CHAPTER TEN

Having Fun with Food

Jessica attended a special class for children with various learning difficulties. Like most of her classmates, Jessica refused to eat anything in the school cafeteria. She, and the other students, brought lunch boxes packed with the brand name processed foods they preferred to eat. At lunch times these children consistently refused to try anything new. Each week Jessica saw an occupational therapist and speech language pathologist who worked to help her choose more nutritious foods as part of her Individual Education Plan (IEP) which addressed concerns about her picky eating through the state's academic standard for health: that every child understand concepts related to "health promotion and disease prevention."

In addition to Jessica's individual therapy sessions, her school therapists ran a weekly "art" group for her classroom. Jessica's favorite project involved "painting" with paints made with syrup from a can of peaches. The students used asparagus spears and potato stamps to make brightly colored pictures while the peaches "swam" in a small fishbowl on her teacher's desk. At the end of the session each student ate a sliced peach "goldfish" from the bowl.

You don't have to wait until you have the whole family trying new foods together before having fun with food in other ways. Introduce thirty minutes of playtime into your daily schedule with your children. Nothing, not even food, will have a more positive outcome in their lives.

Try some suggestions in this chapter for ways to have fun with (and without) food.

Take a look at the "Play and Mealtime Skills" chart from Chapter One to get an idea what kinds of play your child will enjoy. Look at what types of play your child seems to enjoy. Children have a great variation in the ways they grow. Start with the colors where you have highlighted the most activities, then look at the same color rows on the "Games to Play with Food" chart. Choose games in the row above and the row below the row where your child has the most highlights. Your child will most likely enjoy the games that match their emotional and physical "vibrations". I have summarized some "vibrational" stages in the next few paragraphs.

"RED" OR "SENSORY FOCUSED"

Children who approach the world as if every experience was "brand new" learn about the world through their senses. Choose "food" games that emphasize sensory experiences. Use food as a toy to pick up, catch, or roll around. Provide messy foods like purees and bananas to squish and poke and even splash. Play these messy games outside, in the kitchen, or even in the bathtub, where you can clean up more easily. You can hide a cookie under a leaf of lettuce or fly some mashed potatoes around in a spoon disguised as an airplane. Sing food songs and read food stories over and over again. Bang spoons and plates together to make noise.

"ORANGE" OR "MOVEMENT FOCUSED"

Children who focus on coordinating their bodies use the world as an "exercise" gym. They want to move their hands, fingers, feet, legs and bodies to do amazing "new" things. They enjoy using their senses and have a lot more physical skills for exploring. Blow bubbles outside to help a child develop oral-motor skills for chewing and spitting as well as eye-hand coordination skills for drawing and handwriting. Use discarded kitchen utensils, pots, and pans to make "mud" pies with flour[8] and water indoors, or sand and dirt outside. Set up a "percussion" session with pots, pans and a wooden spoon. Use an apple, orange, green pepper, or turnip instead of a ball. You can hide foods and find them, or roll them on the floor. Almost all children enjoy a good game of "chase" so grab a

---

[8] Use cornstarch for gluten-sensitive children.

carrot and a stuffed bunny and run. Get your child to take the carrot and have the bunny chase her to get it back. Take turns.

Once children have some coordinated skills, they take an interest in adult activities. They want to "help" in the kitchen and grocery store. Let your child splash in the dishwater or hold onto a fruit or vegetable while she rides in the grocery cart. Repeat names of foods, kitchen utensils, and talk about everything you do in the kitchen. At this stage children absorb new words like a sponge.

Get a "kitchen center" for your house or make one from a cardboard box. Play "cooking" in the "kitchen center." "Feed" the foods you want your child to eat to her favorite doll or stuffed toy. If your child has a feeding tube, buy a plastic doll, drill a hole, and put a "feeding tube" into the doll. Now you can play games about getting the dolly to "eat" some foods with her tube, and some foods with her mouth. If you make a salad, get your little one to tear up the discarded leaves of lettuce and make a salad for her doll. Children love to finger paint. Take some ketchup or chocolate pudding into the bathtub and have a party. Then follow with a bath to clean up the mess.

"YELLOW" OR "CREATIVITY FOCUSED"

Children with words and reasonably good coordination get really interested in doing what adults and older kids do. They can help pack a picnic lunch to eat at the park, outside in the yard, or at a roadside stop on a trip. Eating at different tables reinforces the "eat at the table" habit. Outdoor barbecues serve the same purpose.

Children love the mystery of how a seed turns into a plant. Put a few bean, radish, carrot or lettuce seeds into a bit of dirt in the yard or a pot in your apartment. Watch what comes up. How does it taste? Don't forget to give it plenty of water, but not too much. If some plants die, put more seeds in the dirt and start over again. Go visit a farm and see where your food grows.

You can make all kinds of interesting art work with food. Carve pumpkins, watermelons, or even peppers into "jack-o-lanterns." You don't have to wait for Halloween (or even celebrate it), but you will get the best buys on "kid-safe" pumpkin carving tools the first week in November. Make use of holiday (holy day) traditions to hide Easter eggs and Passover matzos. Every culture seems to have a custom of hiding some food item for children to find during a special meal. What do you do in your culture? Ask your grandparents what they did as children.

Children who can suck, swallow, chew and breathe without choking can learn how to spit. Spitting games get played outside or in the bathroom where it's easy or unnecessary to clean up. Start by spitting seeds, beans, or smooth toys that are easy to move around in the mouth. Spitting water helps children learn how to manage soft or chewed foods. Show children how to spit into a napkin outside, before they need to do it at the table.

Introduce spitting games far, far away from the table – because they get kind of "gross". Act silly. Practice spitting into a trash can. If you have a food with seeds or pits, go outside and have a spitting contest to see how far everyone can spit. Try having your child chew up some food she likes, then spit it out into a plate and make it into a 3-dimensional picture – like a dog, car or house. These games develop the tongue, lip and cheek muscles necessary for managing to push food out of the mouth quietly as well as for chewing and swallowing.

Once your child has mastered chewing and spitting food into a plate or trash can – show her how to spit food into a napkin. Practice using this skill at the table – first with foods your child likes and then with foods she does not. Use a mirror to show her what she looks like. Work on finessing this skill and reward good performances.

Use vegetable pieces as game tokens in board games. Make "paint" out of canned fruit syrup and food coloring. Asparagus spears make great paint brushes. Paint the bathtub with chocolate pudding, ketchup, mustard, and blueberry syrup before bath time. Read stories about food. Act out stories like the *Hungry Caterpillar* who eats a variety of foods. Make "Stone Soup" out of what you can find in the refrigerator. Build "gingerbread" houses out of graham crackers or sugar cubes and icing. Make bread to eat or use "dough" for making decorations you can paint or decorate when dry.

Children with reasonably good coordination can begin learning helpful chores like putting away dishes and groceries, loading the dishwasher, setting the table, and taking out the garbage. At this stage, your child needs your full attention and supervision for these tasks, but the time you spend now will pay off once she gets old enough to assume responsibility for doing these "jobs" on her own. Children love to help with cooking, adding measured ingredients to a bowl and mixing them works out particularly well at this stage. Let your child try to do what interests her and give plenty of supervision and encouragement as she learns these new skills.

"GREEN" OR "INVENTION FOCUSED"

MY KID EATS EVERYTHING

Once your child can read, write, count, and follow directions you have a real helper in the kitchen. Your child will enjoy taking "responsibility" for taking care of the family, especially if "jobs" come with "privileges." A child who sets the table might get a slightly larger dessert portion, when she puts desserts at everyone's place setting. A child who washes dishes gets to choose the evening movie or storybook. If you make your own sandwich you get to choose what you will eat and maybe even include a cookie along with some fruit. A child who takes out the trash gets to go for a special walk with the "chief cook and bottle washer." Remember to keep it FUN so the job gets done. "Jobs" and "responsibilities" only become "work" when you take the FUN out.

Helen Keller, a blind and deaf woman who brought disability out of back rooms and into public view during the early half of the twentieth century, was asked by a reporter what she would like to see if she could see only one thing. She replied, "The rainbows in the bubbles when I'm washing dishes." Don't forget to look for those rainbows and teach your children to find them, too.

A child who enjoys looking at catalogs can plan and choose which plants to put in the garden. She can assume responsibility for watering the plants and picking off the bugs. By the way, picking bugs off by hand helps with eye-hand coordination and is the MOST organic method of insect control available. Use gloves and a jar of water if squishing them seems too "icky."

Your child can help cook special dishes for meals or parties and enjoy sharing these foods with family and friends even if she won't eat that food herself, YET. Use foods for edible artwork like *"amuse bouche"* delightful single bites of food used to decorate individual plates or spoons and "amuse the mouth" of diners before a meal begins. Japanese food artists make *"bento box"* lunches in containers with dividers. Each section has an animal or flower made from food. An online image search using *"amuse bouche"* or *"bento box"* will pull up more ideas than you can count.

Blowing bubbles with gum continues to develop oral-motor skills and seems "more socially acceptable" than spitting games. If your child has trouble making a bubble in her mouth, have her spit the gum into her hands, make it into a "pancake" with her fingers, wrap the gum around her tongue and hold it with her teeth before blowing air into the gum. Bubble gum bubble blowing makes a great activity for a birthday party. As with all "gross" games, play this one outside only, where messes do not cause as much trouble.

SUSAN L. ROBERTS

"BLUE" OR "CONFORMITY FOCUSED"

Once your child has developed a network of friends her own age, she will begin to question adult judgments and abilities. *The Portable Pediatrician's Guide to Kids* calls this stage "land of the rolling eyeballs." The more closely your child knows an adult, the less likely she will take direction and advice. Random strangers, media personalities, and adult or teen-age friends of the family have much more credibility than parents and teachers, at least in face-to-face encounters. You can hear this same child recommend her parents and teachers as "experts" in the very subjects whose advice she ignored at home or school.

Your child will test her independence and learn better from "real life" experiences than well-intentioned advice. Give her room to make "safe" mistakes and encouragement to clean up her messes so she can learn from these experiences and develop good judgment. Your child will tell supportive adults about EVERYTHING and hide secrets to avoid criticism or punishment. You may struggle watching your child make mistakes and despair over her frequent "lapses in judgment." Remember at this stage she needs to learn judgment from experience. Give her a garden plot of her own. Give her responsibility for making lunches, for herself and the rest of the family. Lavish her with praise for delicious lunches and forget about the "not-so-good" ones. Let her try out new recipes and be prepared with a "back-up" meal if her "experiment" fails.

During the stage when your child develops judgment from experience, she has an enormous need for support and encouragement. Media and peer pressure to have the "right" body type – "model thin" for girls and "buff" for boys puts older children at risk for skipping meals, eating "diet" foods or even taking legal and "illegal" meal supplements (like steroids). Family meals give you an opportunity to observe your child's eating habits for changes and share her day's highs and lows. Sharing meals as a family literally saves children's lives. Have fun with food and make it a central part of your family life.

"PURPLE" OR "RELATIONSHIP FOCUSED"

Once a child can drive a car and make some money of her own, the heavy lifting of parenting has reached completion. Now you can only watch and see what your child makes out of what she has learned so far. If she learns to enjoy sharing food with her family she will continue to enjoy making and sharing meals with her family and friends. Remember the "responsibility/privilege" dynamic. Your teenager, who makes

118

meals, may get car privileges to drive to the grocery store. If she buys groceries, she gets to choose what to cook and eat.

Sharing family meals needs to continue through adolescence and on into adulthood. Paying jobs and school obligations may put a strain on scheduling family meals, but these meals continue to serve as an important time for monitoring eating habits and relationships with friends. Encourage your child to bring friends over for dinner. Be ready to set an extra place, or two, at the table. Your child can help plan menus and cook meals for friends who come to family dinners. Your child may complain about regularly scheduled "family meals" but when her friends say, "I wish my family ate together like yours" you will feel like a "champion parent."

FREQUENTLY ASKED QUESTIONS

Q: My child attends elementary school but she still only eats pureed foods and prefers toys that light up and play music at home. On the card it says toddlers and infants play these types of games. She can dress herself and write her name. I feel silly playing these "immature" kinds of games with her.

Very few children develop with ALL their skills at "age level." (That is, completely matched to their chronological age in every area of development.) Most children develop more uniquely and creatively – so most children develop some skills faster or slower than others. Use your imagination to choose food games your child will like – pushing buttons on a blender or mixing food may be more fun than measuring

Have Fun – Use food in daily play with your child for thirty minutes every day – cooking and cleaning up together counts as play if you are having fun.

Play Safely – DO NOT expect children to eat or even taste "food items" used in play. Make sure all gross games (like spitting games) get played away from the table. Children (or adults) who spit at the table without using a napkin must leave the table at once.

Make Friends – Invite children to join you in cooking, table setting and cleaning up activities.

Use Imagination - Use food items in play. Give children responsibility for "fun" meal related tasks.

ingredients. Making "mud pies" and digging in the garden may be more fun than looking at recipes or garden catalogues. Do what your child enjoys and forget about "typical age" on the chart.

Q: All these games seem so messy. I can't imagine doing them with my child.

If messy games make you uncomfortable, do not play them. You will communicate discomfort to your child. Ask a therapist, baby sitter or another child to play with your daughter while you supervise. Stay in your comfort zone and help your child find hers. Your child may need to get a little messy to get over some texture issues through play before she can put textured foods in her mouth.

CHILD'S PLAY RESOURCES

Introduction to How Does Your Engine Run? The Alert Program for Self-Regulation by Marcia Williams & Sharon Shellenberger. (1996). Therapy Works Inc. Fun activities to teach children about their sensory systems.

The Out of Sync Child Has Fun, Revised Edition: Activities for Kids with Sensory Processing Disorder by Chris Kranowitz. (2006). Perigee Trade. Lots of fun activities that all children can enjoy.

www.zonein.ca – Chris Rowan, occupational therapist, website for how to unplug children from technology and get them more involved in active play.

"Vibration"	Mealtime Behaviors	Outdoor Play & Movement
Red "Sensory"	Frequent "on demand" feedings, Liquids (milk or formula) Pureed foods (after 3-4 months) Messy-food falls out mouth Frequent choking Occasional spitting up Cries for food	Reaches for & grasps bottle, spoon, cup, caregivers hands Explores textures, flavors, smells with hands & mouth
Orange "Movement"	Eats small portions Eats on a schedule Sits in high chair Pureed to soft chopped food Drinks from a Sippy cup Messy-food falls out mouth Squeezes food with fingers Food falls off spoon Prefers single foods Avoids sticky foods Asks for foods by name	Eating snacks at the playground picnic table Making "mudpies" with flour (or cornstarch) and water Splashing water in sink Playing with pots & pans
Yellow "Construction"	Eats small portions Eats on a schedule Sits at a table Eats solid foods Drinks from a cup Uses a spoon Shows interest in a fork Wipes mouth Spills drinks Enjoys dipping foods Asks for food in sentences Says "please", "thank-you"	Eating snacks at the playground picnic table Outdoor barbecues Digging in a "garden" Watering plants with a can Planting seeds Picking fruit & vegetables

© Susan L. Roberts, 2011

WITH FOOD

Social Games with Others	Creative Play & Toys
Food in an "airplane" spoon Peek-a-boo Pat-a-cake Repeating sounds & words	Food songs Imitates facial expressions Explores hands & feet with food on them Bangs utensils to make noise Explores toys with food on them
"Stealing" foods to get a child to try a new food Sharing food Hiding & finding Naming foods Helping with groceries Helping with dishes	Pretend cooking "Feeds" dolls/stuffed toys Play with kitchen utensils Explore foods by tearing them up Scribbles in whipped cream, pudding, ketchup
Sharing food Making Mr. Potato Head Helping w/ jack-o-lanterns Finding eggs, matzoh Use vegetables for games Putting away dishes Putting away groceries	Helps with cooking Stories about food/eating Names pictures of foods Build gingerbread houses Build sugar cube houses Arrange crackers on a plate Draw pictures of food Making foods from dough

"Vibration"	Mealtime Behaviors	Outdoor Play & Movement
Green "Invention"	Small portions get larger Remembers meal schedule Sets table Occasional spills pouring or carrying liquids Learns to cut own meat Clears table Washes dishes Makes own sandwiches Converses at table Remembers "manners" Asks to leave table	Plans garden Digs garden Plants seeds & seedlings Waters plant with can Picks bugs off plants "Mother May I?" manners game
Blue "Conformity"	Portions get larger May "skip" meals Makes own lunch Makes simple dinners Conversations need prompts Forgets "manners" Leaves table to join friends Brings friends home	Can have a small garden Chooses plants Digs garden Plants seeds, seedlings Waters plants with hose Picks bugs off plants Harvests garden produce Dries produce from garden
Purple "Relationship"	Portions get much larger then stabilize May begin "dieting" Makes dinners for family Converses about interests "Manners" better away from home Eats out with friends Cooks meals for friends	Plans more complex gardens May use lawn mower, tractor or other power tools

WITH FOOD

Social Games with Others	Creative Play & Toys
Follows directions for recipes Shares food she made Use vegetables for board game tokens Enjoys cooking classes	Help plan meals & parties Pick out recipes Make food collages Makes "amuse bouche" Makes "bento box" lunches Helps carve "jack-o-lantern"
Cooks with friends Collects recipes Makes food for school Enjoys cooking classes Helps with canning & fermenting	Plans menus Experiments with recipes Puts together appetizer trays
Plans parties with friends Collects recipe books Cans & ferments food Enjoys exotic foods with friends & family Gets a restaurant job	Makes more elaborate recipes Prepares complex meals

CHAPTER ELEVEN

Surviving Holiday Meals

Six year old Tim only liked to eat pizza, cheese-flavored puffs, mashed potatoes and strawberries. He could tolerate most foods at the table, but gagged if a grown-up asked him to "take a bite" of anything. His grandmother had always kept a strict "clean your plate" rule while Tim's mother lived at home. Tim's family lived over a thousand miles away from his grandmother and had never had a Thanksgiving dinner with her. Tim's parents felt very nervous about the upcoming event, but felt uncomfortable refusing to go for one more year.

Tim and his mother planned to make some turkey-shaped appetizers out of strawberries and cheese-flavored puffs in their hotel before going to the meal. Tim's father figured out a way to take slices of pizza and rearrange them into a turkey by adding a carrot for a beak and a cranberry for an eye. Tim's parents practiced table manners with him and warned him that his grandmother might ask him to eat foods he didn't like. Sure enough, grandma told Tim he needed to eat his turkey and cranberry sauce if he wanted to have any pie for dessert. Tim remembered "the magic words". Giving grandma his biggest gap-toothed smile he said, "I love you grandma. Can you please pass the mashed potatoes?" Everyone at the table, including grandma laughed, and the meal progressed without further incidents.

We all want our big family dinners to look like the happy events we see on TV and in movies. Sure, these families have drama occurring, but on the screen, everyone survives the stressful event with laughter and love. Some families have holiday meals devoid of laughter and what love they share gets thoroughly hidden under too many layers of criticism and regrets. If you come from a family like that, bless your picky eater for providing you with an out, and take it. "Timmy gags if there's any meat on the table, so we're skipping Thanksgiving this year."

Hopefully by this time, your picky eater has progressed much farther, but for everyone's sake find a "family" holiday dinner where people laugh and have a good time. You want your children to have pleasant associations with family meals, so avoid toxic holiday meals, especially for your picky eater. Large family meals can be joyous affairs with side dramas and mishaps that lead to laughter and become stories or even legends.

A friend's Seder dinner always included *matzo* ball soup with parsley in it – a deviation from the regular plain soup most people serve. This soup came with a story that did not originate from the Jewish exodus from Egypt, the ritual story told with food during Seder dinner. Every year my friend's aunt made *matzo* balls and carried them to her sister's house to add to the chicken broth. One year her aunt tripped, spilling *matzo* balls all over the freshly mowed lawn. The sisters attempted to pick off all the tiny grass clippings and then gave up and added chopped parsley. After the meal they told the story. The family enjoyed it so much, they tell it every year – and always add parsley to their *matzo* ball soup.

By some unwritten law of nature, even the most supportive of families have at least one "food cop" present at all holiday dinners. This adult loves to comment on what people eat – usually by sharing a story, or five, about mealtimes "back in the day." Learn to laugh at these stories and remember they have nothing to do with you or your child.

Parents of "picky-eaters" often face the traditional family meals with a certain amount of dread. The everyday stress of worrying about nutrition gets magnified wondering if "well-meaning" relatives and friends will trigger a "melt-down" by commenting on a child's refusal to eat traditional family favorites. Even the most jovial of Thanksgiving families sits with tight lips in shocked silence when a "picky eater" gags at unfamiliar sights and smells.

Rehearsing table manners and mealtime skills will help you and your picky eater avoid negative experiences with the "food cops" in your family.

1. Make learning table manners a game and practice playing at mealtimes.

You can award points each time your child remembers to:
- Ask "please pass the ..."
- Say "no thank-you, I'm feeling kind of full..." and pass a dish to the person next to them
- Tell the cook how much they enjoyed eating a dish (even if it means he just didn't dislike it as much as all the other unfamiliar offerings).

Subtract points for:
- Chewing with an open mouth full of food. (Use a mirror so he sees how he looks).
- Complaining about the food.
- Gagging or spitting food onto his plate.

You can use pennies to keep track of points, or toothpicks. Raisins, candy, or small crackers your child can eat at the end of his meal work well to tally points.

2. Practice moving unfamiliar foods around with utensils to make them appear eaten.

All of us learned this trick as children, trying to convince our parents, or teachers that we had eaten a food we didn't want to eat. We squashed the food out flat, scraped it back together in a pile, carved out a "bite", or tucked it under some lettuce. Teach your child this skill and reward him for using it instead of complaining out loud. Friends and relatives will likely forget about a child quietly playing with food, but remember loud complaints, whining or crying.

3. Practice quietly spitting unpleasant foods into a napkin.

Sometimes your child avoids foods he cannot manage chewing and moving around in his mouth. Make sure your picky eater has good enough oral-motor skills to spit unfamiliar foods quietly into a napkin. Give a prize to the family member who can spit a mouthful of food into a napkin without anyone else noticing.

Practice spitting games away from the table to help your child develop these oral-motor skills. Look at Chapter Ten "Having Fun with Food" for more ideas.

4. Use the Role-Playing Game

Share stories about the "food cops" in your family with your child. Tell these stories in a funny way. When we laugh at someone who wants to intimidate us, it takes all their power away. Teach your child to laugh. Children's laughter charms adults.

If you know which "food cops" your children will encounter at a family meal "role play" these encounters. Do funny voices and wear funny clothes to exaggerate the "food cop's" characteristics. Say the kinds of things you think a "food cop" might say. Teach your child the important "magic words" he must say in return. Teach him the responses you believe will work best, that is: the most polite and appropriate responses you can imagine. These "magic words" will protect your child from harmful and hurtful criticism.

5. Prepare & bring a special dish you know your child will eat.

Everyone needs to enjoy holiday meals – and experience that happy, full feeling we associate with big lavish meals. This might mean introducing a new holiday tradition – like pizza, chicken nuggets, or even fish-shaped crackers. Dress up your child's favorite foods to make them more "festive."

Agree ahead of time what level of "trying" new foods will work at your holiday dinners. Can your picky eater just say "no thank-you?" Does he have to push a relative's "special dish" around on his plate? Make sure your child knows that he will get to eat the foods he likes if he "tries" some unfamiliar foods. Let him know he can ask, "Please pass the ..." when he wants the "favorite foods" you have brought.

Oftentimes children enjoy preparing food they don't eat. Have your child prepare a dish he may not have tried, but one you think he would enjoy. Let everyone know that your child prepared this special dish. He may get so many compliments that he tries the dish himself. Even if he doesn't, friends and relatives will remember the dish he prepared rather than the dishes he refused.

6. Turn the meal into a "secret" challenge.

Once you have practiced these skills prior to the big day, let your children know that you have a special "Academy Award" prize that goes to the child whose performance results in a friend or relative commenting on his "good behavior."

Even if you don't actually get a compliment from a friend or relative, make sure you have a prize, like going to the movies, for getting through a holiday meal using good manners and avoiding whining or complaints.

Developing these mealtime skills and rehearsing them will make you and your children feel more in control of the stresses associated with unfamiliar foods. Holiday dinners could lead to all sorts of wonderful opportunities – at restaurants, in school and even more pleasant and relaxed family dinners at home.

FREQUENTLY ASKED QUESTIONS

Q: What exactly do you mean by "role play"? It sounds like making fun of someone. I'm not sure I want to teach my child to do that.

"Role playing" means acting out a predictable and emotionally charged situation as a way to figure out more efficient ways of managing one's emotions when the event actually occurs. For instance you can think of some comments family members might make to your picky eater, like "If you were my child I would make you eat that or go to bed without dessert," or any other such comment that might trigger a "melt down" with your child. Teaching your child some polite responses to deflect attention from his plate could save a holiday meal from disaster. Role playing will take surprises out of critical comments and gives your child a way to feel in control of maintaining his dignity. These "magic words" can help him in other situations as well.

Have Fun – Prepare a special dish (or two) to bring to the holiday dinner

Play Safely – Make sure your child knows the "manners game," can hide food he won't eat on his plate and politely spit food into a napkin.

Make Friends – Role play and rehearse family dinner manners before the big day. Let your child know you will support his food choices at the meal.

Use Imagination – Find creative ways to "dress up" your child's food choices as "holiday" fare.

CREATIVE CHILDREN'S FOOD RESOURCES

The Everything Kids' Cookbook: from Mac n Cheese to Double Chocolate Chip Cookies – 90 Recipes to Have Some Finger-Lickin' Fun by Sandra. K. Nissenberg. Adams Media (2008). A great cookbook for children and adults who want to cook with children.

Yum Yum Bento Box by Crystal Watanabe and Maki Ogawa. Quirk Books (2010). Full of great ideas for decorating foods for children's lunchboxes.

www.aibento.net – Adventures in Bento - a website full of **great** ideas for making fun lunches for children.

CHAPTER TWELVE

What Are Food Sensitivities?

Sixteen year old Barbara had a lot of embarrassment about the intestinal gas that plagued her almost constantly, and seemed intolerable right before her menstrual cycle. She also had problems with her complexion and more than occasional bouts of diarrhea. Numerous visits to the doctor produced various medications that she took for a while and then stopped when none of her symptoms entirely disappeared.

In Barbara's health class the teacher began talking about food and mood changes. He asked all of his students to keep a food log to see if they could detect any effects from eating certain foods. Barbara kept her food log and noticed that she seemed to have more problems with gas after she drank milk, or ate cheese pizza. One week she stopped eating or drinking any dairy products. Barbara noticed less gas but she did not really believe lack of dairy had helped her. On Saturday morning Barbara helped herself to a big bowl of her favorite cereal with milk. She and some friends planned to go out for pizza that evening. Soon after eating the cereal Barbara's gas and diarrhea returned. At dinner she ordered a hamburger, without any cheese. She kept her food choices relatively dairy-free from then on. She enjoyed a calmer digestive system – and felt pleasantly surprised when her complexion cleared up as well.

Everyone seems to have more awareness about food sensitivities these days. We hear about it in the media and from friends and acquaintances. Many families worry about food sensitivities in their picky eater and I often hear families tell me about dramatic improvements in their child's behavior after a sensitivity gets diagnosed and treated.

Perhaps you have wondered about food sensitivities. We mentioned these as a possible reason for children becoming picky eaters in Chapter Two, "Why Is My Child Such a Picky Eater."

I wait until the end of the book to address food sensitivities, because usually our "favorite" foods cause us the most problems. We evolved as omnivores, eating a wildly diverse, seasonal diet and now most of us stick to a much smaller variety of foods. Whenever we eat one food daily or exclusively we run the risk of becoming sensitive to that food. Picky eaters, and especially problem feeders, run higher risks of having food sensitivities, simply because they eat a smaller variety of foods.

Until your child eats a wide variety of foods and more easily introduces new foods into her diet, hold off on exploring food sensitivities, which can change or disappear once your child eats a wider variety of foods. Usually treating food sensitivities means eliminating foods. If your child eats a small number of foods and refuses to try new foods, you could easily take away your child's "lifeline" foods and leave her without the basic nutrition she needs to grow and thrive.

One of the saddest stories I've heard came from a therapist who worked with a family that decided to put their problem feeder on the "gluten free, casein free" diet, removing all wheat and dairy products, including yogurt, one of the five foods this child ate. The child refused to eat any of the new "gluten free, casein free" foods. Month after month she got sicker – skin bruises that didn't heal and big dark circles under her eyes. Finally, three months after beginning the elimination diet, a doctor diagnosed this child with scurvy, vitamin C deficiency, and surgically placed a feeding tube so she could get her nutritional needs met.

Do not begin any elimination diet without consulting with your family doctor. He can do a number of tests to determine if your child has a specific food "allergy," that is, a response to a food that produces a significant number of "histamines" or other "allergic" reaction markers. Once you have eliminated foods from your child's diet these tests will no longer be accurate, even if you re-introduce the foods. So test first, eliminate later.

If you suspect a food sensitivity, watch how your child responds to different foods as she eats them. The "Food and Mood Journal" form can help you do this. Blood tests can discover "allergies" but some mild food sensitivities go undetected, and still cause symptoms. The "Food and Mood Journal" helps you determine if you have negative reactions to certain foods.

Take a look at the "Most Common Foods Causing Allergies and Sensitivities" table to get an idea which foods might be involved. Read the list of possible symptoms. Print out the "Food and Mood Journal." Write down what your child eats, then let her rate the foods (or rate them for her if she cannot do it herself).

Immediate enjoyment, gives us the first window of truth. "Do you really LOVE this food or do you eat it out of habit?" Generally, foods we really enjoy are foods that nourish our bodies. The foods we eat out of habit, or because of a craving for sweets, may not taste as good as we imagine when we pay close attention.

After about half an hour our bodies respond to what we have put in our stomachs. We may start to see symptoms that soon, or we may not see them until two hours later. Fill out the "Food and Mood Journal" just before having another meal or snack to see if any symptoms have occurred. Keep the journal for several days to get some ideas if symptoms occur with the same foods.

Sometimes symptoms do not show up for a few days which make it harder to tell which foods cause which symptoms. As an adult who wants to verify that a food causes certain symptoms, you can eliminate that food from your diet for a week or two. Do the symptoms go away or increase? For some people the first few weeks after eliminating a food cause an increase in symptoms. With your child you want to avoid eliminating foods unless you have the support of your doctor or a registered dietician.

If you have eliminated a particular food for three months without seeing any noticeable difference in symptoms, your child most likely does not have a "sensitivity" to that food. Do not eliminate foods unless your child has a food sensitivity or food allergy. All foods have nutritional value. Removing foods does not prevent food sensitivities from occurring.

Once a food that causes sensitivities gets taken out of a diet, reintroduction can cause a dramatic increase in symptoms. If symptoms suddenly return during an elimination diet, look for a slip-up. Review all the foods eaten in the past 24 hours and see if any have elements of the sensitive food. Look for the most likely culprits in processed foods which mix in a variety of food "additives".

Many people report recovering from food allergies and sensitivities by following a diet of "GI tract-healing" foods for six-months or several years. Often these people return to eating small quantities of the "trigger" foods. Some people learn to live with a few "mild" symptoms whenever they choose to experience a food they love. Each person and family must make their own choices about how to handle food sensitivity.

If you have a picky eater you suspect has food sensitivities, get some experienced help with eliminating foods. NEVER eliminate foods from a problem feeder's diet without help from a registered dietician or experienced nutritionist familiar with elimination diets. You run the risk of causing serious illness. Eliminating foods always benefits from expert advice and support.

If you do not know any registered dieticians go to www.eatright.org the website for the Association of Registered Dieticians. If you put in your zip code they can give you names of dieticians in your area. Find one who is familiar with food sensitivities.

Have Fun – Approach the challenge of exploring food sensitivities food with curiosity and a sense of adventure.

Play Safely – Pay attention to the way your child feels after eating (or not eating) certain foods. Get help to explore cooking and eating with food sensitivities.

Make Friends – Do the food and mood journals as a family and share your results with each other at mealtimes. Find a support group – even if it's online.

Use Imagination – Revisit your menu plans and make adjustments to cut out foods which make family members sensitive. Eat offending foods at restaurants so temptation doesn't take a daily toll on food sensitive family members.

Elizabeth Strickland, a dietician and nationally known lecturer, has written, *Eating for Autism: The 10 Step Plan to Help Treat Your Child's Autism, Asperger's or ADHD*. She does not address food sensitivities until step seven and eight. If you think your child has a food sensitivity, read this book and follow her plan through all of the steps. Ms. Strickland also has a website.

If your child goes on the most common gluten-free, casein free diet and you don't know what kinds of food to make at home check out www.whattofeedyourkids.com for some recipes. Leanne Ely from Saving Dinner (www.savingdinner.com) also has special bundles of recipes for elimination diets of various kinds. Sharon Kane from Food as Medicine can teach you how to make all whole grain gluten-free sourdough breads, pancakes and muffins through her website, www.the-art-of-gluten-free-baking.com.

Please make use of these resources to help your child with this complicated area of nutrition.

FREQUENTLY ASKED QUESTIONS

Q: My doctor does not believe in testing for food sensitivities, what can I do?

Try looking for another doctor willing to explore food sensitivities with you. You can also find registered dieticians and nutritionists who have experience with food sensitivities and elimination diets. Read Eating for Autism by Elizabeth Strickland or What's Eating My Child by Kelly Dorfman (mentioned in resources for Chapter Three). Explore the topic online. Always get an experienced professional to guide you when it comes time to eliminate foods from your child's diet.

Q: I'm thinking of eliminating foods from my child's diet and I cannot find a professional in my area to help me with this. What should I do?

Chain in all the "substitution" foods you will introduce into your child's diet before eliminating anything. Make sure that your child eats ALL of these "new" foods before subtracting any foods. You can find recipes for these "new" foods in books about food sensitivities. You can also work with nutritionists and dieticians who will work with you over the phone. Look for help from experienced professionals by reading books and searching online resources.

FOOD SENSITIVITIES RESOURCES

Eating for Autism: The 10-Step Nutrition Plan to Help Treat Your Child's Autism, Asperger's, or ADHD by Elizabeth Strickland. (2008). Cambridge: Da Capo Lifelong Books.

SUSAN L. ROBERTS

The Body Ecology Diet: Recovering Your Health & Rebuilding Your Immunity (10th Ed.) by Donna Gates. (2006). B.E.D. Publications.

www.whattofeedyourkids.com - Gluten-free, casein-free, dairy-light information and recipes.

Common Sense Approach to Discovering and Treating

Food Allergies & Sensitivities

1. Observe and document what you eat and how it makes you feel/behave. How do you feel/behave when eating the food? How do you feel/behave within 30 minutes of eating the food? How do you feel/behave 2 hours later?

2. NEVER, EVER eliminate a food from anyone who eats fewer than 40 different foods without the assistance and supervision of a Registered Dietician. You can find one by going to www.eatright.org.

3. Go after the biggest target – What do you eat most often? Reduce that food first and see how you feel.

4. Before trying any food elimination – try preparing most of your food at home. Eliminate processed and prepared foods first as these contain the most additives.

Dried beans as well as whole grains (like wheat, rye, barley, oats, brown rice & quinoa) have lots of anti-nutrients that protect these seeds from being digested. All of these foods do better with a traditional preparation – i.e. soaking in water with a spoonful or two of vinegar or yogurt for 6-24 hours prior to cooking

Most Common Foods Causing Allergies & Sensitivities

The following eight foods cause 90% of all the food allergies in the US – according to the Food Allergy & Anaphylaxis Network – www.foodallergy.org

Food	% of Population Affected[1]	Possible Sources[2]	Symptoms[3]
Wheat	10	All **gluten** containing products including wheat, rye, barley, spelt & sometimes oats. Also in ice cream, sauces, play dough, potato chips, rice cakes, turkey patties, hot dogs	**Ears** – otitis media (ear infections) **Nose** – nasal congestion, sneezing, runny nose
Milk	2.5	Look for **lactose, casein, & whey** - common additives derived from milk. Milk, cheese, yogurt, butter. Also sometimes deli meats, tuna fish.	**Eyes**- tearing, puffy eyes, dark circles under eyes **Oral** – swelling of lips, tongue, mouth, & throat
Shellfish	2.3	Shrimp, crab, lobster.	
Fish	2.3	Salmon, tuna, halibut. Watch out for salad dressing, Worcestershire sauce, BBQ sauce, bouillabaisse, and imitation fish products.	**Skin** – hives, eczema, red cheeks, itching **Respiratory** – difficulty breathing, cough, wheezing, asthma
Eggs	1.5	Look for egg additives in foam on drinks, egg substitutes, pastas, pretzels.	
Peanuts	1	Look for peanuts oil & other peanut additives in sauces, puddings, cookies, hot chocolate, glazes, marinades, Asian foods.	**Intestinal** – reflux, vomiting, nausea, abdominal pain, diarrhea, constipation
Soy	1	Look for hydrolyzed soy proteins, soy oils and other soy additives in **everything**.	**Neurological** – headache, migraine, & behavioral problems such as tantrums, irritability, & hyperactivity
Tree Nuts	0.006	Walnuts, almonds, hazelnuts, coconuts, cashews, pistachios, Brazil nuts. Look for nut additives in salads, salad dressings, meat-free burgers, pasta, fish dishes, honey.	

---

[1] Exact figures not available, these approximations were gathered from a variety of sources and are meant as a guide to prevalence of the allergy in the general population.
[2] From Food Allergy & Anaphylaxis Network – www.foodallergy.org
[3] From *Eating for Autism: The 10-Step Nutrition Plan to Help Treat Your Child's Autism, Asperger's or ADHD* by Elizabeth Strickland, MS, RD, LD

MY KID EATS EVERYTHING

Food & Mood Journal

Name: _____ Start Date: _____ Finish Date: _____

Date	Food Eaten	Immediate Enjoyment Behavior	30 Min Later Feelings Behavior	2 Hours Later Feelings Behavior

Immediate Enjoyment: 5 = Yummy – the best food ever / 1 = Yucky – I never want to see it again

Feeling: 5 = Feeling Fine – happy & full of energy / 1 = Hungry, headaches, shaky & grouchy

Behavior: 5 = Calm, content, focused / 1 = hyperactive, irritable, distractible, tantrums

SUSAN L. ROBERTS

CHAPTER THIRTEEN

Saying Farewell

I hope you have enjoyed your journey to adventurous eating so far. Have you transformed your mealtimes from battlegrounds to family sanctuaries, or are you still setting the groundwork for family mealtimes that everyone enjoys? Even if you meet once a day to share some animal shaped crackers and a glass of milk you and your family will reap a long term benefit from "breaking bread" together.

Have you learned something about your picky eater, yourself and the rest of your family members? Food changes everything. Sharing food builds bonds even among strangers. Every religious tradition has stories about the importance of welcoming a stranger by sharing hospitality.

Have you found out that your child's picky eating has reasons you never expected? If you needed support to address your child's needs, I hope you have found loving and supportive professionals to guide you on that journey.

Has food become more interesting as you examined textures, flavors, smells, colors and shapes with your picky eater? I believe each of us enters this world with lessons to learn and lessons to teach. Teaching always requires more from us than learning. Has your picky eater taught you to appreciate food and food choices in new ways? If you find your child has made some progress, but the going still seems slow and tough, remember this. Have patience. Once he has encountered all the important people – doctors, therapists, relatives and teachers – who need to learn from him the doors will open to a world of easy mealtimes and adventurous food choices. I call this a "teaching contract"[9] and I believe that your child has a contract he will honor throughout his lifetime. You cannot rush that process. Relax and let it happen at its own pace. Enjoy the time you have with your child and honor your "contract" to feed, clothe, educate and learn from him. Know that you have done your best and that in spite of all your best efforts your child has his own life path to follow. Keep mealtimes simple and friendly. Provide the healthiest choices you can. Let him choose *whether* to eat and *how much.*

Become your child's partner in this effort. I believe he chose you because he knew you would provide the support and challenges he needed to learn his lessons and complete his "teaching contract." Every holiday meal, birthday party and church picnic provides a new opportunity to educate others about the importance of respecting our food choices. Each new professional you encounter on your journey to heal your child's body and improve his ability to make more friends, puts you in a place to learn and to teach. Respect those moments and trust your instincts about when to move on when your child needs a different approach or technique.

Have Fun – Eat what you love. Love what you eat.
Play Safely – Trust your child's food choices. Trust your own food choices.
Make Friends – Eat with family members and friends whenever possible. It heals your body and your soul.
Use Imagination – Try new foods. Variety is the spice of life.

You know enough to make the rest of this journey on your own. Godspeed!

FREQUENTLY ASKED QUESTIONS
Q: Where can I go to get more help?

---

[9] For more information on life "contracts" I recommend reading Carolyn Myss' book *Sacred Contracts: Awakening Your Divine Potential.* You can also find a brief summary of this concept at www.myss.com/library/contracts.

Review the list of helpful professionals and when to get help from Chapter Two. To find professionals in your area contact : occupational therapists through *www.aota.org*; speech and language therapists through *www.asha.org*; registered dieticians through *www.eatright.org*. Many children with autism or related behavioral challenges find help through the National Autism Association, *www.naa.org* and through Autism One, *www.autismone.org*. Talk to other parents. You will find the help you need. Many professionals work by phone and over the internet. You can get help everywhere. Do not give up. Keep hope alive. Food changes everything.

If you have any more questions or want to let me know about your journey, contact me on Facebook and let me know. You can also reach me at my e-mail address: *susan@susanlroberts.info.*

A FEW MORE RESOURCES
Sacred Contracts: Awakening Your Divine Potential, by Carolyn Myss. (2003). New York: Three Rivers Press. A wonderfully empowering and creative approach to exploring life's challenges.

The 3-Season Diet: Eat The Way Nature Intended to Lose Weight, Beat Food Cravings & Get Fit, by John Douillard. (2000). New York: Three Rivers Press. Information and recommendations about the benefits of adjusting your diet to reflect seasonal changes.

Engaging Autism: Helping Children Relate, Communicate and Think With the DIR Floortime Approach, by Stanley Greenspan, MD. (2006). Cambridge: Da Capo Lifelong Books. The Floortime approach encourages parents to take an active role in helping their children through playful activities.

Real Food on a Real Budget: How to Eat Healthy For Less, by Stephanie Langford. (2010). Keeper of the Home Publishing. How to find bargains and affordable choices when eating organic and traditional preparations of food.

www.food-medicine.com – The Art of Gluten Free Sourdough Baking – Sharon Kane's excellent resource for gluten-free sourdough whole grains recipes.

<u>www.nutritiondetectives.com</u> – David Katz, MD – Free curriculum for teaching children about nutrition.

APPENDIX A

Sugar by Many Other Names

Sugars are carbohydrates made up of one or more molecules. **Glucose**, **fructose** and **galactose** are single molecule sugars (monosaccharides) that occur naturally or through manufacturing processes. **Sucrose**, **lactose** and **maltose** are double molecule sugars (disaccharides) made up of various combinations of glucose, fructose and galactose and they also occur naturally or through manufacturing processes. Starches consist of multiple sugar molecules (polysaccharides) that allow plants to store excess sugar. Normal digestion and manufacturing processes break these starches into simpler forms of sugar.

Our bodies require glucose as fuel and all cells in our body can metabolize this sugar into energy. Ribose and deoxyribose are sugars that make up our RNA and DNA. Our bodies process and recombine the foods we eat to make these essential sugars. The following list defines many common foods and food additives containing sugar.

Agave nectar or **agave syrup** is commercially produced from several species of agave plants. Agave nectar is sweeter than honey and thinner in consistency. Agave nectar consists primarily of *fructose* and some *glucose*. The exact percentages vary from vendor to vendor.

Brown rice syrup is made by fermenting cooked rice with enzymes (usually from dried barley sprouts) to break down the starches, then straining off the liquid and reducing it by cooking until the desired consistency is reached. The final product is 45% *maltose*, 3% *glucose*, and 52% maltotriose (a trisaccharide made up of three *glucose* molecules).

Brown sugar consists of sugar crystals contained in molasses syrup with natural flavor and color made from sugar cane. Some refiners make brown sugar by adding syrup to refined white sugar. It is 91% to 96% *sucrose*.

Cane sugar, **cane crystals** and **evaporated cane juice** come from the processing of sugar cane into the white crystal we know as table sugar, 100% *sucrose*.

Confectioner's sugar, or powdered sugar, consists of finely ground *sucrose* crystals mixed with a small amount of cornstarch.

Corn syrups, corn sweeteners and **crystalline fructose** are produced by the action of enzymes and/or acids on cornstarch, splitting that starch into sugar components. They contain between 42% to 98% *fructose*. Dextrose, water and trace minerals comprise most of the remaining ingredients.

Dextrose, a form of *glucose*, is commercially made from corn starch by the action of heat and acids, or enzymes. It is sold blended with regular sugar.

FRUCTOSE consists of one sugar molecule found naturally in honey and fruits, such as apples, grapes and peaches. Fructose has a much sweeter taste than sucrose. Fructose requires the liver to metabolize it into usable energy for the body. A synthesized version of fructose, refined by the food industry decades ago, created a product known as high fructose corn syrup.

Fruit juice concentrates made from dehydrating fruit juices and using them as sweeteners contain primarily *fructose*.

GALACTOSE is a single molecule sugar that occurs naturally in the body and combines with *glucose* to form *lactose*, the sugar found in milk.

GLUCOSE is a single molecule sugar occurring naturally in all living organisms and used by all of them as fuel for life. Manufacturers create glucose by processing starches from a wide variety of plants including corn, maize, rice, wheat, cassava, corn husk and sago.

High-fructose corn syrup (HFCS) is a sweetener made from cornstarch. The amounts of *fructose* vary with the manufacturer. An enzyme-linked process increases the fructose content, thus making HFCS sweeter than regular corn syrup.

Honey is an invert sugar formed by an enzyme from nectar gathered by bees. Honey contains *fructose, glucose, maltose* and *sucrose*.

Invert sugar is a mixture of *glucose* and *fructose*. Invert sugar is formed by splitting sucrose in a process called inversion. This sugar prevents crystallization of cane sugar in candy making.

LACTOSE, or milk sugar, is a double molecule sugar consisting of *glucose* and *galactose*. It occurs naturally in the milk of mammals. Lactose is manufactured from whey and skim milk for commercial purposes, primarily used in the pharmaceutical industry.

MALTOSE is a double molecule sugar consisting of two *glucose* molecules. It occurs naturally in the fermentation of barley grains and through caramelizing (heating sugar until it turns brown). The body breaks maltose into glucose very easily and rapidly.

Malt syrup is made from sprouting, fermenting and caramelizing grains such as barley, and wheat. The primary sweetener in these syrups is *maltose*. They also contain starch and a little protein.

Maple syrup and sugar is made by boiling the sap of the sugar maple tree. This sweetener contains mostly *sucrose* with small variable amounts of *glucose* and *fructose*.

Molasses is produced as a by-product of processing of sugar cane. The quality of molasses depends on the maturity of the sugar cane, the amount of sugar extracted, and the method of extraction. **Blackstrap molasses** contains the least amount of sugar as well as trace amounts of vitamins and significant amounts of calcium, magnesium, potassium, and iron; one tablespoon provides up to 20% of the daily value of each of those nutrients

Raw sugar consists of coarse, granulated crystals of *sucrose* formed from the evaporation of sugar cane juice. Raw sugar contains impurities and cannot be sold in grocery stores due to FDA regulations.

Sweet sorghum syrup or **sorghum molasses** is made from sorghum (in the same grass family as sugar cane) in much the same way molasses is made from sugar cane and sugar beets.

Sucanat and **Rapadura** are brand names for a variety of whole cane sugar extracted by mechanical processes, heated, and cooled, forming small brown grainy crystals of pure dried sugar cane juice. These brown crystals, similar to **panela** and **muscovado**, retain their molasses content.

SUCROSE, **or table sugar**, comes from sugar cane or sugar beets. It consists of two simple sugars, *glucose* and *fructose*. It is about 99.9% pure and sold in either granulated or powdered form.

Turbinado sugar is raw sugar that goes through a refining process to remove impurities and most of the molasses. It is edible if processed under proper conditions; however, some samples in the past contained trace contaminants.

APPENDIX B

Sugar Substitutes

Sugar substitutes, also called artificial sweeteners, take the place of sucrose (table sugar) and other sugars (see Appendix A) to sweeten foods and beverages. The U.S. Food and Drug Administration (FDA) regulates artificial sweeteners through the Food Additives Amendment to the Food, Drug and Cosmetic Act, passed by Congress in 1958. This law requires the FDA to approve food additives, including artificial sweeteners, before they can be made available for sale in the United States.

Studies show conflicting evidence of potential harm caused by sugar substitutes. Most have little or no calories, so contribute nothing in terms of nutritional value to our foods. Many are made from ingredients we would never consider eating under normal circumstances. Recent studies indicate that despite their lack of calories, most sugar substitutes seem to contribute to weight gain rather than prevent it. Sugar substitutes do not seem to contribute to tooth decay as sugars do.

The following list gives the names and some information about common sugar substitutes approved by the FDA.

Acesulfame K, sold under the trade names Sunett and Sweet One, was accidentally discovered by a chemist in 1967 and is widely used in foods, beverages and pharmaceutical products around the world. It is

180-200 times sweeter than sucrose (table sugar), as sweet as *aspartame*, about half as sweet as *saccharin*, and one-quarter as sweet as *sucralose*, and has a slightly bitter aftertaste, especially at high concentrations. Blending it with other sweeteners (usually sucralose or aspartame) gives it a more sugar-like taste as each sweetener masks the other's aftertaste and/or makes it taste sweeter than its components. It can be used in baking and is often used to sweeten protein shakes or make chewable and liquid medications more palatable.

Aspartame, sold under the brand names NutraSweet, AminoSweet, Equal, and Candarel, was first synthesized by a chemist in the course of producing antiulcer drug candidates in 1965. It is found in approximately 6,000 consumer foods and beverages sold worldwide, including (but not limited to) diet sodas and other soft drinks, instant breakfasts, breath mints, cereals, sugar-free chewing gum, cocoa mixes, frozen desserts, gelatin desserts, juices, laxatives, chewable vitamins supplements, milk drinks, pharmaceutical drugs and supplements, shake mixes, tabletop sweeteners, teas, instant coffees, topping mixes, wine coolers and yogurt. It breaks down when heated and loses much of its sweetness making it less suitable for baking than other sweeteners. When eaten aspartame breaks down into natural residual components, including aspartic acid, phenylalanine, methanol, and further breakdown products including formaldehyde and formic acid. Because its breakdown products include phenylalanine, aspartame must be avoided by people with the genetic condition phenylketonuria (PKU).

Cyclamate has been banned by the FDA for use in the United States, but is used as an approved sweetener in over 55 countries including Canada where Sweet'N Low and Sugar Twin contain cyclamate. It was discovered in 1937 by a graduate student working in the lab on the synthesis of anti-fever medication. It is 30–50 times sweeter than sugar making it the least potent of the commercially used artificial sweeteners. It is often combined with other artificial sweeteners, especially saccharin; the common mixture of 10 parts cyclamate to 1 part saccharin masks the off-tastes of both sweeteners. It is less expensive than most sweeteners, including sucralose, and can be used in cooking and baking.

Maltitol, a sugar alcohol or polyol, made from maltose has 75-90% of the sweetness of sucrose (table sugar) and nearly identical properties, except for browning. Used to replace table sugar because it has fewer calories, does not promote tooth decay, and has a somewhat lesser effect on blood glucose, it is known under trade names such as Maltisorb, Maltisweet and Lesys. Like other sugar alcohols, large quantities can have a laxative effect.

Mannitol, another of the naturally occuring sugar alcohols or polyols, can act as diuretic agent and weak renal vasodilator. It was originally isolated from the secretions of the flowering ash, and can be synthesized through the hydrogenation of fructose or extracted from a wide variety of plants.

Neotame, produced by the NutraSweet Company is the most recent addition to FDA's list of approved artificial sweeteners and was developed specifically as an artificial sweetener. Food manufacturers find it attractive for use in diet soft drinks and low-calorie foods because it lowers the cost of production compared to using sugar or high fructose corn syrup (due to the lower quantities needed to achieve the same sweetening). The body appears to rapidly metabolize, completely eliminate and not accumulate this sweetener.

Saccharin, sold under the brand name Sweet'N Low was discovered by a chemist working on coal tar derivatives in 1878. Commercialized not long after its discovery, it took sugar shortages during World War I to reach widespread use. Its popularity further increased during the 1960s and 1970s among dieters. Saccharine, used to sweeten products such as drinks, candies, biscuits, medicines, and toothpaste, is much sweeter than sucrose, but has a bitter or metallic aftertaste, especially at high concentrations.

Sorbitol, is a sugar alcohols or polyols metabolized slowly by the body. Obtained by reduction of glucose sorbitol is found in apples, pears, peaches, and prunes. It is also sold as glucitol, Sorbogem and Sorbo.

Stevia, the common name of *stevia rebaudiana*, grows in subtropical and tropical regions of North and South America. As an herb it is used by native healers to treat diabetes. The herb can have a bitter or licorice-like which diminishes somewhat with low concentrations of the extracts. Stevia leaf may be ground into a green powder or appear as white powder or liquid extracts. It is sold under a variety of names – Truvia, PureVia, Steviva, SweetLeaf – among others. Sometimes stevia gets

153

combined with dextrose or other products to give it more bulk. Read the product ingredient labels and try different brands for taste.

Sucralose, sold under the brand name Splenda, Sukrana, SucraPlus, Candys, Cukren and Nevella, discovered in 1976 by scientists researching ways to use sucrose as a chemical intermediate in non-traditional areas. It has no nutritive (or caloric) value as the body does not break it down and excretes it whole. It also does not readily break down in the environment and is currently found in wastewater. Sucralose does not react to heat or melt allowing it to be used in cooking and baking recipes which do not require caramelizing sugar. Sucralose is often mixed with maltodextrin and/or dextrose which adds approximately 2-4 calories per teaspoon however the FDA allows for any product containing less than 5 calories to be labeled as "zero-calorie".

Xylitol is a naturally occurring sugar alcohol sweetener. Usually made from hardwood or maize, it is found in the fibers of many fruits and vegetables, and can be extracted from various berries, oats, and mushrooms, as well as fibrous material such as corn husks and sugar cane bagasse (maize and sorghum husks also used to make biofuels). Xylitol is roughly as sweet as sucrose with only two-thirds the food energy. Use may result in temporary gastrointestinal side effects, such as bloating, flatulence, and diarrhea, which will diminish with frequent consumption. It has been shown to benefit dental health in humans but can be toxic to dogs.

BIBLIOGRAPHY

Albi, J. and Walthers, C. (1996). *Glorious Greens: More Than 140 Ways to Prepare All Those Great-Tasting, Super-Healthy, Beautiful Leafy Greens.* New York: St. Martins Griffin. We could all use some more delicious and affordable leafy greens in our diets.

Dorfman, K. (2011). What's Eating Your Child? The Hidden Connections between Food And Childhood Ailments: Anxiety, Recurrent Ear Infections, Stomachaches, Picky Eating, Rashes, ADHD, And More. New York: Workman Publishing. A comprehensive look at all ways food can affect children's behavior with practical suggestions for parents.

Douillard, J. (2000). *The 3-Season Diet: Eat The Way Nature Intended to Lose Weight, Beat Food Cravings & Get Fit.* New York: Three Rivers Press. Information and recommendations about the benefits of adjusting your diet to reflect seasonal changes.

Eisenstein, C. (2003). *The Yoga of Eating: Transcending Diets and Dogma to Nourish the Natural Self.* Washington, DC: New Trends Publishing. Letting go of expectations and enjoying the experience.

Fraker, C.; Fishbein, M.; Cox, S.; Walbert, L. (2007). Food Chaining: the Proven 6-Step Plan to Stop Picky Eating, Solve Feeding Problems, and Expand Your Child's Diet. Da Kapo Press.

Gates, D. (2006). The Body Ecology Diet: Recovering Your Health & Rebuilding Your Immunity (10th Ed.). B.E.D. Publications.

Greenspan, S. (2006). *Engaging Autism: Helping Children Relate, Communicate and Think With the DIR Floortime Approach.* Cambridge: Da Capo Lifelong Books. The Floortime approach encourages parents to take an active role in helping their children through playful activities.

Kaufman, B.N. (1995). *Son-Rise: The Miracle Continues.* HJ Kramer Publishing. The story of how one family transformed their own lives and went on to help others through the Son-Rise Program®

Klass , P. and Costello, E. (2004). *Quirky Kids: Understanding and Helping Your Child Who Doesn't Fit In – When to Worry and When Not to Worry.* New York: Ballantine. Two pediatricians with a common sense approach to childhood difficulties.

Klein, M.D. (2003). *The "Get Permission" Approach to Mealtime and Oral Motor Treatment.* Tucson, AZ: Mealtime Notions. This video shows parents and professionals how to get a child's permission to move forward at mealtimes.

Kranowitz, C. (2006). The Out of Sync Child Has Fun, Revised Edition: Activities for Kids with Sensory Processing Disorder. Perigee Trade. Lots of fun activities that all children can enjoy.

Lair, C. (2008). *Feeding the Whole Family: Recipes for Babies, Young Children, and Their Parents.* Seattle: Sasquatch Books. Great recipes for nutritious child-friendly meals.

Langford, S. (2010). *Real Food on a Real Budget: How to Eat Healthy For Less.* Keeper of the Home Publishing. How to find bargains and affordable choices when eating organic and traditional preparations of food.

Louv, R. (2008). *Last Child in the Woods: Saving Our Children from Nature-Deficit Disorder.* Chapel Hill, NC: Algonquin Books of Chapel Hill. Documents how much outdoor play time children have lost; what research says about the benefits of outdoor play; and creative ways communities have acted to increase outdoor play for children.

Miller, L. and Fuller, D. (2007). *Sensational Kids: Hope and Help for Children with Sensory Processing Disorder.* Perigee Trade. Full of insights about how children organize information about the world using their senses.

Myss, C. (2003). *Sacred Contracts: Awakening Your Divine Potential.* New York: Three Rivers Press. A wonderfully empowering and creative approach to exploring life's challenges.

Nathanson, L. (1996). *The Portable Pediatrician's Guide to Kids: Your Child's Physical and Behavioral Development from Age 5 to Age 12.* New York: Collins. You can find lots of books on young children, but this book provides a great overall common sense approach to school age children.

Nissenberg, Sandra. K. (2008). The Everything Kids' Cookbook: from Mac n Cheese to Double Chocolate Chip Cookies – 90 Recipes to Have Some Finger-Lickin' Fun. Adams Media. A great cookbook for children and adults who want to cook with children.

Pollan, M. (2009). *In Defense of Food: An Eater's Manifesto.* New York: Penguin. An insightful look at what we eat from a journalist who has traveled the globe exploring food.

Roth, G. (2010). *Women, Food and God: an Unexpected Path to Almost Everything.* New York: Scribner. How to pay attention and enjoy what we eat.

Satter, E. (2008). *Secrets of Feeding a Healthy Family: How to Eat, How to Raise Good Eaters, How to Cook.* Madison, WI: Kelcy Press. One of many books by this author. It pretty much covers everything.

Siegal, B. (1986) Love, Medicine and Miracles: Lessons Learned About Self-Healing from a Surgeon's Experience with Exceptional Patients. New York: HarperCollins Publishers Inc. A wonderful book about the healing power of love.

Strickland, E. (2008). Eating for Autism: The 10-Step Nutrition Plan to Help Treat Your Child's Autism, Asperger's, or ADHD. Cambridge: Da Capo Lifelong Books.

Watanabe, Crystal; Ogawa, Maki. (2010). *Yum Yum Bento Box.* Quirk Books. Full of great ideas

Williams, M. and Shellenberger, S. (1996). *Introduction to How Does Your Engine Run? The Alert Program for Self-Regulation.* Therapy Works Inc. Fun activities to teach children about their sensory systems.

www.aibento.net – Adventures in Bento - a website full of great ideas for making fun lunches for children.

www.asdpuzzle.com – Elizabeth Strickland, R.D., nutritionist – has articles and offers consultation services via phone.

www.autismtreatment.org – Son-Rise – chock full of wonderful information and tips that will help all parents, especially those whose children have special needs.

www.eatright.org – The American Dietetic Association website has resources including how to locate a registered dietician in your area.

www.ellynsatter.com – Ellyn Satter's website – more information than you can imagine on all aspects of eating, relationships during mealtimes, and how to enjoy the food we eat.

www.food-medicine.com – The Art of Gluten Free Sourdough Baking – Sharon Kane's excellent resource for gluten-free sourdough whole grains recipes.

www.gnowfglins.com – God's Natural Organic Foods Grown Locally and in Season. – cooking courses, videos, information and recipes for simple and delicious traditionally prepared foods.

www.greensmoothiegirl.com - Green Smoothie Girl – information and recipes for kid-friendly vegetables & raw foods.

www.mealtimenotions.com – Mealtime Notions – products and information from Marsha Dunn Klein, occupational therapist and mealtime expert.

www.nutritiondetectives.com – David Katz, MD – free curriculum for teaching children about nutrition.

www.popsiclecenter.org – Parent Organized Partnerships Supporting Infants and Children Learning to Eat – a source for stories, information and support

www.savingdinner.com – Saving Dinner – menus, recipes & shopping lists for making simple dinners at home.

www.tabletopics.com. Table Topics – source for cards that help get conversations started at mealtimes.

www.theboxgirls.com. The Box Girls – a source for cards that help get conversations started at mealtimes.

www.westonaprice.org – Nourishing Traditions – website based on nutritional information derived from population studies done by Weston A. Price, DDS, begun in the 1930s. The site also provides access to recipes and other websites about traditional foods and food sources.

www.whattofeedyourkids.com – What to Feed Your Kids – Gluten-free, casein-free, dairy-light information and recipes.

www.zonein.ca – Chris Rowan, occupational therapist – tips and courses on how to unplug children from technology and get them more involved in active play.

Made in the USA
Charleston, SC
09 September 2016